יהודית

© 2022 Farlag Press
All rights reserved.
Originally published as יהודית : אַ געשיכטע פֿון ליבע און לײַדן
Yudis: a geshikhte fun libe un laydn
By פֿאַרלאַג מײַזל עט קאָ
Maisel & Co., New York, 1911.

ISBN: 9791096677108

English translation © Jessica Kirzane 2022.

An excerpt was previously published as "You Should Have Been
There" in the 2020 translation issue of *Pakn Treger*.

www.farlag.com

MIRIAM KARPILOVE
Judith
A Tale of Love & Woe

Translated from the Yiddish by Jessica Kirzane

Farlag Press

Contents

Notice

Toward the end of May, 1909, the newspapers reported a case of suicide concerning a young man, no more than thirty years of age, whose body was recovered in a remote corner of Central Park with gunshot wounds from a revolver.

A calling card was found in the pocket of his coat, bearing the name Joseph Goldschmidt and an address in Harlem.

An investigation uncovered that the suicide victim was a Jewish intellectual from a wealthy family in Russia, who arrived in New York a short time ago to pursue a career in journalism. A bundle of letters was discovered among his papers. The letters were addressed to him in Russia, each written in the same woman's handwriting. These letters are published here in fulfillment of the wishes outlined in the deceased's will, which, in a few moving lines expressed his desire to make the letters available to the public as a memorial to the broken heart of an innocent woman.

1.   *April 13, 1904*

To my beloved Joseph,

Writing—taking my thoughts and feelings and breathing life into them as letters and words! How hard it is to express in a letter all that fills your soul. But you express yourself so well, Joseph!

If you could have seen the way I read your letter, you would have loved your "proud, stern queen" and would have forgiven her that it took you so long to win her heart.

"I don't belong to myself. My soul, my very being, belongs to you. However much I might talk of myself, *I* am no longer here. My self is annihilated when I think of *you*, my heart's delight!" What beautiful words, *my* Joseph! What pleasure it gives me to transcribe them!

I have told no one of my joy. I've hidden it deep in my heart. I don't want *our love* to get tangled up with all the common gossip that is spread around our town. How unlucky are those who have no secrets to hide!

If only I could express, the way you can, everything that I felt when we parted. But I will never, *never,* forget those precious moments! Time passes so fast. It seems just a moment ago that Aaron first came to tell us his cousin was coming to our town for his sister's wedding. Everyone was eager to see you as we'd already heard so much about you. When the evening of the wedding arrived you weren't here. Then we received a telegram saying that you were delayed, but on your way! My heart was pounding and I asked myself: What does this guest have to do with *my* heart?

When you arrived, all eyes were on you. You took one look at us with smiling eyes that seemed as though they were looking for someone in particular—*me.* Now we know that to be true. Your heart directed your eyes to me. Your gaze rested upon me with astonishment. We were introduced to each other. Our 'intelligentsia' gathered around us and carried on a lively conversation. The midwife complained to you about the backwardness of our small-town life; the teacher lamented that we lack a group for the study of political economy. Berman, also a teacher, bewailed the neglect of modern Hebrew as a language. You heard them all out and then remarked that there was such a congenial atmosphere here and spoke to us about new movements and strivings, about the question of Jewish nationalism.

Your voice was gentle, strong, and warm. It crept into the hiddenmost corners of our hearts. I felt in your words the precarious situation of the Jews, and the urgent need for action.

When the conversation ended you approached the window I was standing near and we both looked out onto the street where the last soft flurries of snow fell and disappeared like the smoke from the chimneys of the houses. Our eyes met and in silence we pressed one another's hands in parting.

A few days later, Aaron's announcement of your impending departure wiped the smile from my lips. You noticed this, and what's worse, you were happy about it. You said if it were possible to start organizing a nationalist group here soon, you might be able to stay until it was done.

"How long do such things take here?" you asked.

"If we put all our energy into it," I responded hesitantly, "it could soon be accomplished." Deep in my heart, I secretly wished the work would take a long, long time.

"Would *you* contribute to the work so it would go faster?"

"Oh, I'm not much of a do-er," I answered.

"What do you mean, a do-er?"

"The work takes two different kinds of people. There are those who think and those who take action."

"So that means that you must be a great thinker."

"A great thinker," you repeated to yourself. Aaron left the room. I felt that your eyes were on me even more than before. I was warmed, illuminated by your gaze. It made me proud and a little unsettled.

"You have such a strong profile," you sighed. "You are like Judith who beheaded Holofernes. Would you have been capable of it?"

"To save my people—yes."

You said at that moment you felt like falling on your knees before me. I looked holy to you. How swiftly you swept me up and kissed me! Those kisses sealed the bond between our two hearts, and from then on, "I don't belong to myself when I think of you, my heart's delight . . ."

Your Judith

2.   *April 15, 1904*

My Joseph, how I long to be beside you! I would comfort your fevered head with soft caresses and beg you to rest.

Your parents won't force you to tie yourself down to a career or coerce you into marrying for money. No, they love you too much. You judge them too harshly. Why can't you understand that they want to keep you with them, out of love for you, and not to give you up to—me? Oh, you wonderful, capricious boy!

Do they know about me yet? You told them—you did! I understand, Joseph, everything that you didn't write. I understand how much they don't want me.

They want a wealthy girl. To what end? They're wealthy enough themselves. In our small town my family is considered among the most well off, but compared to yours . . . No, there shouldn't be rich and poor. Everyone should be equal.

Do you know what my father said yesterday? He said that one day you'll be a famous man, a great public speaker! Do you remember that one time he was so taken by your speech that he grasped both of your hands and said, "Young man, we are very much in need of men like you! Older men, like me, look to young ones like *you* to carry on our work! But you need to be more careful with your words. We must guard our words in this land of spies and unrest."

You stood there and didn't say anything. Everyone stopped talking. You looked into his eyes. Then you lifted your head and swore that you would defend our people to the death.

How strong, how handsome you were, Joseph! How moving it was to see the two of you united in one purpose. I wanted to hold you both in my arms and kiss you, but I was too shy. Why are we always ashamed to give way to our noblest feelings?

Aaron is here. I am sure he is talking about you. I will listen to what he has to say.

I haven't written to you in so long! Aaron stayed for tea. He said that when you graduate with your medical degree you will go away to a village to devote your life to the service of the peasants. My father was up in arms about it. "What do you mean, peasants? Aren't there enough sick people amongst the Jews? Why do you need to take care of peasants?" he asked.

"What difference does it make who the sick are? Should a doctor choose who to help?" my mother asked. "If it's peasants, then let it be peasants!"

"Peasants are peasants. What else could they be? But he certainly could choose if he wanted to. He would be better off studying to be a rabbi."

"There's more wisdom in medical science than in rabbinics," Aaron retorted.

"Is that so—science! They're running off in search of foreign wisdom before they taste that of their own fathers. They don't realize how foolish they are. I thought he wanted to stay here and teach. He doesn't know what he wants! One day he's teaching lessons and the next he's a doctor . . ."

"Delivering speeches, enlightening others, is more than just teaching lessons," said Aaron, who was growing insulted.

"It's all the same. One teacher is just like another, only he's a few dozen years younger than our *melameds* and has new methodologies."

"For instance, our *melameds* could never become doctors, but he can," my mother retorted.

"He can! You don't know what he can do, and neither does he. He's nothing but a firebrand! One day they're one thing, the next day they're interested in something else. There's no commitment. They go where the wind blows. A strong wind comes along and they catch a cold that cools down their fire . . ."

I laughed. Whenever he tries to convince my mother of anything he brings in an example with a chill, an illness, something that she would never argue against.

"Why are you laughing?"

"You're being ridiculous," answered my mother. "Why are you getting so worked up about this? You're just jealous of the young. You wish you were in their place."

"In their place! Do they have a place? Today they're here, tomorrow they're somewhere else. One day they're in seventh heaven and the next day they're six feet under.

Yesterday a rabbi, today an engineer, tomorrow a professor, the day after a lawyer, and now what, a doctor? Well, how is he going to do it? You have to be accepted somewhere first, don't you?"

"In a university," Aaron said. "And before that you have to prepare."

"Where? Here? Forming organizations, stargazing, and enlightening young women?"

"If you want to learn, you can do it anywhere," Aaron retorted.

"Yes, yes, of course. Certainly, at least for peasants, any quack can be a doctor."

Berman, who had been quiet this whole time, asked me if you're thinking of coming back here. I told him yes, and then I felt so despondent.

Joseph, I'm so afraid that your parents won't let you come here. What do they, wealthy as they are, want from you there? But they will come around. Yes, how can they help it if you love me? Oh, Joseph, I can't write any more. It pains me that I, the source of your suffering, cannot be there to assuage it.

Your Judith

3. *April 18, 1904*

What makes you think that my parents will object to a man whose future prospects are still distant? That they want me to marry a "finished man" who is already beginning a career? Even if that were true, what does that have to do with us? Joseph, you must know that no one in the world could change my feelings for you. My poor, dear man, how you suffer! How can you love someone so much and still be uncertain of her certitude? Oh, Joseph, in your love for me you overlook my love for you! My darling, why do you torment yourself with misgivings? Berman, Aaron, this one, that one, you worry that they all love me. And what if they do? I love you, do you understand? You, and you alone!

What a rich imagination you have, Joseph, and how excitably you rush to conclusions. Just wait, I will calm your restless spirit with news from the "New World." My mother has a sister in America, no, a step-sister, and she hadn't received a letter from her in years. A letter came yesterday, saying she heard our iron foundry is not doing well. We should sell everything and come to America, "where it is easy to get things settled for your girls." If we can't all make the journey at once, she wrote that my parents should at least send one or two of their girls, the oldest of course.

My uncle, her husband, buys and sells houses. "They're worth a few thousand dollars," she says, and he can care well for his nieces. Should I go, Joseph? What do you think? You know that if I even considered it, all I would have to do would be to take one look at my father, and I would collapse with regret. My father was enraged at the suggestion. "Send away the girls!" He said he'd write to my aunt and tell her to send some of her own girls to us instead. He'll find them appropriate matches.

Joseph, have you ever seen a better father? Aside from you, I love him more than I love anyone. He is often angry, but never at me. I'm his favorite, his treasure.

Berman came in just as I had finished reading your letter. He said, "Angels are dancing a *kamarinskaya* across your face; your eyes glow with a poorly hidden joy; your laughter is bright, your steps as though keeping the beat to a song, every room that you enter is illuminated." Your very words! And yet what different things they mean! Perhaps they have the same ardour, but I don't feel it the same way because *you're* the man I love, only you.

My friends used to call me a "cold angel." If only they knew what a hot, passionate love lies in the heart of this "cold angel." My love, my soul is only known to you, and no one else. You say you know my soul even better than I know yours, but I don't like that. Is your soul too distant or too elevated for me to reach? But I am glad that at least you understand *my* soul. I understand why you love me, since you know it so well. Joseph, everyone knows that I have a high opinion of my own soul. I love it. You don't even know how good it is. I want you to know even the most hidden corners of my soul. Then you would see how completely it is filled with you. Oh, Joseph, as much as you speak of your love for me, it cannot be stronger than my love for you. What are you feeling now? Write to me. Do you still have your headaches?

My dear Joseph, you told them everything so quickly. Didn't you have any time to slow it down? Maybe it's better that they already know. Oh, things will get better. They *must*. We love each other. We have a right to be happy!

Your Judith

4.   *April 19, 1904*

How can I respond to you? I long for you so. I cannot express in words everything that I feel. Last night I cried in my sleep. I dreamt that someone was trying to tear you away from me while you were holding me close. I clung to you, but the force that drew you from me was stronger than us both.

It's good that I received your letter today, Joseph. Without it, after such a night, the day would have seemed too empty.

Do you know, Joseph, how jealous I am? And of whom? Of myself. I feel like I am two different people: the person I show the outside world, and the person I am inside. On the outside I am pretty, on the inside I am good. The outside says she's the one who caused you to love me, and if she, the pretty one, were to vanish, then the good one would be left powerless to attract. The inner one is jealous of the outer one.

Which of them is right? Joseph, my love, tell me.

I can't write any more today. Such doubts creep into my head. Joseph, I long to see you, to talk to you, to know you better.

Your Judith

5. *April 20, 1904*

I thought I would get a letter from you today, but none came. I'll write to you in the meantime. I need to write to you.

I wonder what you are doing at this very moment. You

didn't write anything about your parents in your last letter. Have you won them over, or are they still so strongly
opposed that they won't even talk about it? My parents
complain that I spend too much time lost in thought.
Maybe I should tell them. I don't even know what words
I would use to begin. I am too timid, despite my six years
in gymnasium. Do you know, Joseph, it bothers me that
I didn't complete all seven? That would have been quite
a culminating accomplishment, don't you think? But
I could no longer tolerate the antisemitism. One girl,
Anyuta or, as she used to call herself, Ana Andreyevna—
you know who I mean, the lively blonde girl you met
here at your uncle's pharmacy—never suffered from
antisemitism. She associated with the antisemites and
joined in their insults and jeers. One of her brothers is
baptized. She used to say that she wanted to convert
too. She advocates assimilation, says we must lose our
"characteristics" and stop being middlemen, exploiters,
swindlers, and all the other words they use about us.

What do you think of that?

She told me once that one of the other students in the
gymnasium, a "gentleman," sought my acquaintance. He
was worried that I was avoiding him because I disliked
Christians. I told her that I don't hate Christians. The
next day she led the "gentleman" to me together with
her own sweetheart. When she introduced the man to

me, she said that he was infatuated with me.

The tall "infatuated" student with a pale freckled face blushed, bowed deeply, and held fast to the hand I politely offered. Her sweetheart, a Polish-looking boy who was head over heels for her, suggested that we all go for a stroll on the boulevard together. I excused myself, saying that our horses were waiting for us (Anyuta and I used to ride home together), and my parents wouldn't know what to think if I were late. The Polish boy threw her a meaningful glance and she tried to convince me to stay in town. She didn't want me to ride alone and leave her behind, and anyway it wasn't nice not to agree to such a harmless little thing. I told her that it wasn't good to make my parents worry on account of such a harmless little thing. We rode home. We didn't speak to each other the whole way home. When we arrived, she told me, "Tomorrow I'll apologize to them for introducing them to such a *zhidovka*! You're nothing but a Jew!" With that, she left.

Can you imagine how I felt? She's now living in ____, a city not far from yours. I hear that she is active in secret revolutionary circles, and has dozens of darlings, sweethearts, and "gentlemen."

Why am I writing you all this? What use is it to you? I had better go to bed and fall asleep with the hope that I'll receive a letter from you in the morning. Good night!

❖

It's nine o'clock at night and I am only just now ready to send off my letter. What should I do with the rest of my evening? Read, and read some more. I can hardly stand it. If *you* aren't the subject of my book, it doesn't interest me.

You told me you were charmed by a story because it was about a character with my name who had deep black eyes, arched eyebrows, and long, long hair. I'm grateful she was only a character in a book, because if not, I would be . . . Don't think that I'm not the kind that can get jealous, or that I don't have an opportunity to experience that emotion just because you never give me a reason to! You yourself even told me that jealousy is a deeply buried instinct, that it is totally blind. It doesn't need a reason. I have an imagination, I can create my own reasons.

I think if someone had told me before that I would be so completely in love, I wouldn't have believed them. I've been told that I rely too much on logic, and until I'm able to lose control of my reason I will never be able to love with my whole heart. That's not true. I can see now that I love you with my whole heart, my whole soul, and my whole mind.

Your Judith

6.   *April 21, 1904*

Joseph, I have been to the post office three times today and there was no letter from you. Tonight I will cry myself to sleep again. It was all I could think about today, and I was so anxious. Something must have happened to you. You wouldn't make me wait without a reason. You know how hard it is for me. Send your answer soon.

Your Judith

7.   *April 22, 1904*

Still no letter. Joseph, I'm worried and angry at you. Either you're unwell or you've simply grown tired of writing to me every day.

I would have had so much to write to you today, if only you had written to me. But as it is, I'll just wait.

I lie with my eyes closed and I imagine I can see you, your arms outstretched, calling out to me quietly. In my mind I draw closer to you, and you hold me fast in your arms. I tremble. My eyes open. The vision has flown away.

With love from your –
Judith

8.   *May 5, 1904*

Receiving your letter . . . didn't cheer me very much. Hope deferred saps the heart. You didn't write because you didn't want to dispel the feeling that I was with you. You were so close in your imagination to me that you felt as though you were truly kissing my hair, tasting my breath, speaking to me, to my spirit.

Really, Joseph, to my spirit?

My inner self is insulted. My spirit should have refreshed your memory, should have told you to be strong and not to lose your nerve.

Don't love me with a love that's so "deep, wild, and strange"! Your love frightens me. It is too intense. It burns you up, it devours you.

How do I love you?

Without all of that tumult, and yet intensely. My love is deep and calm. There is no corner of my heart or mind that does not belong to you. Oh, it is the richest, most wonderful feeling I possess. It is my own. I guard it inside of myself as a miser watches over his wealth.

Oh, my Joseph, you ask if I understand how much you long to hold me in your arms and carry me off somewhere far away, to live only with love. But that is impossible. Do we need to have all that? Joseph, my parents won't let me go without any promises, and your parents will have to finally acknowledge that our love is stronger than death. Don't be so carried away with love, my dear Joseph!

Misha asked me, "When will Joseph come back? He promised to teach me many things."

I responded, "Isn't Berman enough of a teacher for you? Oh, you just don't like that he's angry when you don't do your lessons well.

"He is cross even when I know my lesson. He laughs at me and doesn't teach me anything. He hates me. He hates everyone. He even hates you. When I ask him something while he sees you walking by, he doesn't say anything at all."

My father entered and asked Misha if he'd said his prayers yet.

"Yes, I said them, but just the first few prayers of the morning service."

"Just the first few? Why not the whole thing? Judith, you're spoiling him. Do you know what this young man, only barely past his bar mitzvah, has been up to? Crawling up on the roofs, busy with the pigeons, like all of the other naughty boys."

As a punishment, my father told him that he wouldn't buy him a pony (which is what Misha had been asking for), and I, to make things easier on him, gave him a kiss (thinking the whole time of you, and how he loves you. I don't kiss for nothing.) He's always talking about you. He misses you, and he helps me miss you too.

My mother called us to eat, grabbed Misha, threw my father a meaningful glance, and left the room.

"You know, Judith," said my father, "you should try to cheer up. How about celebrating Misha's birthday?"

"It was nine months ago!"

"In that case, maybe there's another excuse to be happy? "

"Does there need to be an excuse?"

"What do you think there needs to be?"

"A *reason,* I think."

"Don't you need a reason to be unhappy, too?"

"Oh, father . . ."

"Father, father, don't father me, but tell me the reason. Out with it! What is the source of your sadness?"

In my mind I had a notion that I might tell him, but my heart interceded on its own behalf, demanding that I never reveal it, that my precious secret should not become public property for all the world to enjoy.

"Is there no reason? Surely there must be something you want? A dress, a hat, a ring? "

"A pony! Two ponies! One for me and one for Misha!"

Misha ran toward us, and I threw my arms around him and spun around crying, "Ponies for us both! We will ride together far away into the forest!"

He was delighted and echoed, "Far away, far away! All the way to Joseph!"

"Did you ask her? What did she say?" my mother pressed my father.

"Did I ask her? What should I ask her? I didn't ask anything. Come and eat, children! Heniya, Rokhl, Shimka, everyone come to the table!"

Misha sat at the table with eyes that called out, "A pony! A pony!" and my eyes answered his with "A letter! A letter from Joseph must be coming soon!" And it turned out to be true! Oh Joseph, there is nothing better in the world than a letter, a letter from you . . .

I thought about giving you a taste of your own medicine. I was going to make you wait a long time for an answer. But I simply *cannot.* And I beg you, Joseph, don't make me do it anymore either. Don't make me wait. Write, write, until you can come to me Joseph, my Joseph.

I won't write any more to you today. Instead I will *think* of you.

Your Judith

9.   *May 9, 1904*

My Joseph, I will write to you only briefly today. We're going to a fashionable entertainment in town for a charitable cause. My father and I are going together, with Heniya and Berman. I'm taking your letters with me and will be thinking of you the whole time, and kissing you in my thoughts.

If only you could see me! I am dressed all in white. I look very pretty. It's a shame that there's no reason to look pretty if you aren't here to see it.

Your Judith

10.   *May 12, 1904*

Joseph, I didn't want to tell you this, but I *must*. I don't want to withhold from you something that you must know, something that you must respond to. I opened a letter that had a stamp from your city, and it was a letter from your parents to mine. They blame my parents for fooling their son, taking advantage of his naïveté and turning him against his parents. But, they say, they don't want to fight and are going to take the high road. They are going to have to give in, one way or the other, sooner or later. They offer to give my parents as much money as it will take to convince them to part ways with their son for good. My parents will never have you for a son-in-law; they shouldn't delude themselves.

Oh, Joseph, imagine if my parents had read the letter!

Joseph, maybe you have regrets? A promising future is laid out before you—should you give up on it because of love? Is it worth so great a sacrifice? Will I be able to give you enough happiness to make up for it? Think it over and tell your parents. Tell them that you can–if you can–do what they ask of you. Maybe you'll be able to forget about me soon enough. You will be free from your "heart's desire" that brings with it so much misfortune, from your "bright shining star" who, in shining, leads you off your path in life.

If only you can forget all about me, it isn't too late. Oh, maybe you aren't as far gone as your parents think . . .

Your Judith

11.   *May 17, 1904*

Joseph, my dear, my love, my heart—forgive me!

I will never write such a thing again. "Forget me" is such an easy thing to s*ay*!

I thought your parents were going to take you away from me. Your protests did not ring true. Your words about "strength of character" seemed to be merely a cloak for weakness.

I didn't tell you everything they wrote. They wrote asking if something happened between us, because of my own *frivolity* . . . Oh, Joseph, you have no idea how much sleep I lost waiting for your letter to arrive!

Even after all this, I can't think ill of them. They are, after all, *your* parents. However calculating they are, they do love you. You saw how upset they were when you refused to talk to them and threatened to leave home after you were rattled by my telling you to forget me. "Do what you like," they told you, even if it was only begrudgingly.

Give my love to your sister. I love her for loving us both. Isn't it something, how the little girl sympathizes with us! She even snooped and told you that they rummaged through our letters. Pinch her little cheek for me, to thank her for spreading the word.

Joseph, how I long for you. A strange sort of despondence has come over me. I just want to sit beside you, hear your voice, feel your hand in mine . . .

Your Judith

12.   *May 23, 1904*

How happy I am that I, and only I, am the one who brings you joy!

You asked me if I am drunk from our love, or if I am *entirely* swallowed up by it? No, my dear sir! My love is sober, full of thought and feeling. And it isn't true that my love for you and yours for me hasn't fanned the flames of my love for anyone else—quite the opposite, it has only strengthened it. Now I want to embrace the whole world! Because you love me, I have come to love myself so dearly that soon all I will be able to do is give myself compliments, hold my own hand, look into my own eyes and speak directly to my own soul.

You don't know what your love does to me. Any more of it and I'll truly turn into the angel you say I am. Whenever I think of you I do so many good things.

Oh, my dear, it is so good to be good, when you are happy!

So, your parents are satisfied with my lineage? I come from a family of rabbis, merchants, doctors, and American millionaires. "And if we stubbornly hold back, maybe they'll throw in a few thousand more for the dowry," your parents say. Oh, my dear, I am not angry at them for saying so.

Can it be that you will be here soon? Oh, Joseph! It's

spring, and it's beautiful here, and everything is good. We could spend whole evenings and nights strolling, paddling in boats, climbing mountains! But no, you have to study. I will help you! I will go to you, quietly, and stand behind your chair breathlessly, and watch you sit and prepare for your exams. Sensing my presence, you will wrap your arms around me and hold my head *tightly* between your hands and seal my lips in a long, long kiss before I run from your room. You will try to pull me back to you but you won't be able to . . .

Good bye for now, and . . . come to me! I will do everything I can to deserve the name that you gave me: Your "shining star,"

Judith

13.   *June 1, 1904*

What a surprise! How handsome, how terrifically handsome you are! And what a wonderful idea you had to photograph yourself looking at my picture! The photograph looks as though it's speaking. It has so much character, so much life! It's not just a picture of your outward appearance, it's a photograph of your heart, of your soul!

I'm sending you a flower from my flowerpots. You should see how prettily they bloom! Such fine red, pink, and white flowers. I kept this white one under my pillow all night long. I send my kisses to you with it. Oh, how sentimental I am! See, how white, how innocent it looks. They say that a red flower is a symbol for passion. I love this white flower. It isn't so ostentatious and provocative. It is pure and subdued. It strokes you with its soft white petals and beseeches you to be calm, calm . . .

This is the kind of flower you need, Joseph.

As for the alarming rumors that Aaron sends you about our city, unfortunately I have to confirm that they are true. The *chinovnik* who is posted here, they say, was sent to incite a pogrom. They've organized a self-defense league that has thirty-three members.

I don't want to write any more about that. All I want to do is look at the picture of you with your –

Judith

14.   *June 17, 1904*

Of course, Joseph, I will write to you about everything if that's what you want. The *chinovnik* was here and told us that he had to follow his "duties as a police officer" to assess the worth of the householder and—his pretty daughters.

He demanded money for the Red Cross, for those

wounded in the war with the "damned Japanese," and he spoke about Russia in a tone of distress, saying that "if it weren't for us" all of Russia would now be in the hands of foreigners. Foreigners take everything and . . . now as for the rebels, how many are there? Now, even for example in a small town like this one, it's impossible to tell how many there are . . . "

"It's impossible to count a sum that amounts to nothing," my father answered.

"Nothing? Ha! I know your kind are fond of hiding your sins . . ."

"Do you know anyone who likes to keep them out in the open?"

"Heh heh heh . . . hmmm . . . But you know, my brother, this is no joking matter. We ought to gather up these traitors from their hiding places and make an accounting of them. Heh, heh, who knows if there aren't some right behind me, right here. Maybe there's a boy hiding here, sticking out his tongue at me, or showing me his fist. Heh heh . . . "

"Why should a *chinovnik* be bothered by a Jewish tongue or fist?"

"Well said, brother! We're not afraid of such things. But a *chinovnik* must have eyes in the back of his head. Do you know what? I will take a certain sum of money from you to support a group of true Russian patriots who are defending Russia from undesirable elements. That way we can stop rebellions, for instance if your people in the mill, or in the ironworks, should try to go on strike . . ."

"I can deal with my own people myself. I don't need to pay a band of hooligans for that."

"What if they make demands?"

"That's nothing. I'd be better off giving them, my own people, the money they demand than giving it to some hooligans."

"That is against the law! I'm here to carry out police orders and I will report any illegal activity that occurs, even if it were done by a misguided Russian Orthodox Christian. Don't you want to prevent another Kishinev? You, you . . ."

We heard a terrible blow. My mother and I were sitting in another room. I jumped up and ran to my father's office. The *chinovnik* stood in front of my father. My father's hand trembled as it rested on a side table that usually held an encyclopedia. The encyclopedia was on the ground.

"Oh, mademoiselle, my regards!" the *chinovnik* cried.

My father's glare ousted me from the room. The *chinovnik* soon went away, leaving my father fuming. My father went to the governor to appeal to him for protection in the event of trouble. He reprimanded me for showing myself before such a mongrel, and forbade me from leaving the house.

I look out onto the street and see people crouching in fear. They talk to one another only with their eyes. The air is full of anxiety.

Good night, Joseph, and may it be a night without dreams. You are right, even a good dream is no good, because when you wake nothing remains. Nothing? No, the pleasant memory remains. Even if it's the memory of a dream, when we have so little that's good in reality.

Your Judith

15.   *June 12, 1904*

You make me afraid with your fears about me! You paint the picture too black. I give myself over to your fears and instead of giving me strength, you make me lose heart.

You are afraid because I am a member of the self-defense league. That's what I thought you'd say! Would you rather I be without a weapon?

Last night my father distributed arms to the self-defense league. His hands were trembling, but his voice was firm as he spoke to us. He forbade us from using the weapons except when we have no other choice. We should not spill any innocent blood, we should only act in self-defense. We are too few in number, and too weak, for vengeance.

We left the armory quietly. We saw no one. Even the moon was hidden.

Joseph, I'm afraid only for you. Your wanting me to be calm shows me how upset you are. How did you allow those—what do they call themselves?—to leave something like that in your home when so many houses are being searched? Maybe they wouldn't investigate your house because of your parents' reputation, but Joseph, on principle you should not have done it. You are against terrorism. You spoke so strongly against introducing such measures into the Poalei-Tsiyon movement, because it could tear the movement apart. How could they have let you take something like that? Did they force you to do it? No, forcing you would have been against *their* principles.

If I find myself in danger, of course I'll send you a telegram, so you can come. For now, stay near, because I'm so afraid, Joseph, that you'll be carried away by the tide. No, you won't get drawn into the current. You are strong, strong enough to stay behind with those who are weak.

Your Judith

P.S.: It was too late to post this letter last night so I kept it overnight and in the meantime I received another letter from you. You asked after me, and I know that you're hiding something about yourself, something secret. You write so little.

Nothing new happened here overnight. The troubles are restrained, held at bay. All we can do is wait.

16.   *June 16, 1904*

Yesterday I waited all day for a letter from you and it still hasn't arrived yet today. I'm worried. The general atmosphere here is tense. Every little thing that happens here is taken to be a signal that there will be a pogrom.

No one has seen the *chinovnik*. They say he wears a disguise.

It's as though we've been imprisoned. Our parents won't let us leave the house.

The signal that we need to act in self-defense will be— the danger itself.

Answer my letter as soon as you can. Write quickly, if you haven't already.

Your Judith

17.

June 25, 1904

Yes, Joseph, in just a few words you reassured me. How difficult it was to wait! But what does that matter now? It's over.

If you want me to believe that it isn't so bad in jail—I will believe you. There's one thing you are safe from there—a pogrom. We are still not safe from that here. They're dragging it out. What are they preparing for us? Who knows?

Your Judith

18.

June 28, 1904

I never imagined that a jail could be so good! So you are no longer alone? Yes, a few companions certainly makes it merrier. Send my greetings to the whole company. Thank you especially for the greeting you sent from Anyuta—Ana Andreyevna. Why should I be surprised? If you can end up in the same city, why shouldn't you end up in the same jail?

Last time I wrote very little because I was in a hurry to get to the post office in time, and I was too agitated having read about your being in jail . . .

Your Judith

19.   *July 1, 1904*

How long will it be, Joseph, until they let you free? How long is the punishment for standing in the street and reading out a proclamation? I hope you will be free soon.

I won't write any more. Forgive me for writing so little.

Maybe the storm will break tomorrow. That's what they say. And maybe nothing will happen.

Your Judith

20.
                                               July 8, 1904

You're home! Now I will write more to you. Oh, Joseph, how much I suffered knowing you were in jail! And why? To what end?

Truth be told, it doesn't matter to me who you were in jail with. And it doesn't bother me that Ana Andreyevna didn't care for my cold greeting. I don't want to write about her. There are more important things to say.

What we were waiting for finally happened. It began in the morning of July 3rd, and it did not let up until the night of the 5th. Eleven people were killed. Almost all of the stores were ransacked. The number of wounded is immeasurable. So many people moan or stare with silent agony, biting their lips, clenching their fists, lying helplessly on the ground.

Our ironworks was almost the first business to be looted. To carry out their devilish work, they needed weapons: knives, axes, and iron bars. The "poor innocent peasants" made off with iron plows. Who knows how much they will sweat over their "mother earth," plowing it with our plows, breaking it up with our harrows, fertilizing it with our blood and marrow . . .

And Jews will pray for a good harvest, and our liberal, broad-minded youth will help the poor peasants and praise the peasant spirit, their open, innocent souls . . .

Don't ask me for the details of what happened. I can't describe it. It's hard to move my hand to write it down. My eyes look without seeing, my mind thinks without being able to recall.

I saw the places where the worst of it happened. One woman told me that they trampled her child under their feet. I heard of another whose misfortune was even more unthinkable. No, don't ask. I cannot tell you the details.

At one time I wanted to telegraph asking you to come. But I couldn't send you a telegram in jail. My heart ached thinking of you with that hearty, enthusiastic company. I felt I was a stranger to you. I felt that you were joining their ranks, going away from me to them . . . And do you know, I decided then and there to stay with my own, even if all that remained of them was graves. I would stay to look after the graves.

My mother, Rokhl, Heniya, and Shimka are scared out of their senses. Misha clenches his fists and swears on his portion of the world to come that he will take vengeance when he grows up. My father paces back and forth across the rooms of our house in a heavy silence. We are ruined. It's hard to conceive of such a quick downfall from a wealthy household to an impoverished one.

My father's creditors, themselves ruined men, came to us to ask for money. My father paid with his daughters' dowries.

Good night, Joseph, don't make me wait long for my only comfort, your beloved letter to –

Your Judith

21. *July 16, 1904*

Write to me, Joseph! Your writing revives me, brings me to my senses and nearer to you. It thaws the ice that encases my soul.

Yes, love me, love me as hard as you can. And don't ask me what else I need from you. I don't need anything more from you than your love.

I won't entertain the thought that my parents would be willing to accept a loan from yours. I don't want that. If my father needs money, he'll get it from his former business associates. We are ruined as far as possessions are concerned, but he still has his good name.

Borrowing money from you . . . And I thought you wanted to hide our poverty from your parents. What a comfort it is to me that you love me so! "Even more so in your times of trouble," you write. Oh, I would be even more misfortunate, if it meant you would love me more!

In the dark night, as I sit alone by my window, I call out to you in the silence. If you could come, I would take your hand and lead you to where those horrible things happened. I would take you to the graveyard, where a fresh mountain of earth lies over recently buried bodies. We would stand there and listen to the murmur of the trees, the mysterious silence of the dead . . . Will you come?

Your Judith

22. *July 18, 1904*

So your parents know about our poverty? And they are angry because we have nothing? They're right to be upset, Joseph. You seem all too happy about it.

Now they won't want anything to do with me. What will we do? We can cry, we can beg for their permission, or we can carry on without their gracious approval .

If we just talk matters over, you write, we'll figure out what to do. We'll find a way to live without anyone's help. Oh, Joseph, if you could say what you wrote to me in your letters instead of just writing it, how far I would be from thinking about anything practical! I would follow you with my eyes closed into your dreamy fantasy world.

But putting fantasies aside, I have a practical plan. Let's go to America. I won't tell you everything that I'm imagining for us there, how happy we would be there. I want you to decide whether or not to go based on your own understanding of how it could be.

I anxiously await your reply.

Your Judith

23.   *July 20, 1904*

Forgive me, Joseph, I didn't realize that it was out of the
question. I didn't know that you can't afford the journey.
We could economize. We could go, as others do, in second or even third class? I'm not so delicate that I will
only travel in first class.

Joseph, I think class seems to play too large a role
for you. And your fear of the unknown in a strange
land, your fear of being independent, is also too great.
Independence is something to fight for. You aren't used
to that. Don't make excuses.

You must understand, when you consider traveling,
that I'm not the kind who would be a great burden on
you. But it seems that you aren't interested in America,
and I won't ask you to go anymore.

Today I received a letter from America. My relatives
want to send me a steamship ticket. I think I will tell
them to send it. It is good for a whole year. Who knows,
maybe it will become *necessary* for me to use it. Or maybe it will come in handy for *you.*

Be well, and don't worry. I am not angry with you. You
were right to tell me the truth about how you feel. I can't
write any more today, I have a headache.

Yours, with all my heart –

Judith

24.   *July 24, 1904*

Oh Joseph, you're silly to thank me for loving you, and for being afraid that I'd be angry with you, even a little!

I have no good news to write to you today. Last night nine houses next to ours went up in flames, and our house was half destroyed by fire. We all barely escaped, although later a burning piece of the rafters fell and hit my father in the head, and now he's lying in bed.

I cannot write anymore. I have to go be at my father's side. He is distraught. Everything in our half-burned house looks tragic. Be well and write to me of better things.

Your Judith

25.   *July 28, 1904*

No, Joseph, we won't get anything from the insurance company. The policy recently expired. We should have renewed it, but the situation was so tumultuous that we forgot.

Don't despair? I won't. My only concern is for my father. He is unwell.

I haven't slept in two nights. Today I will stay up with him again. He sleeps poorly, or not at all. He looks around and thinks. We try not to let him think.

It's four o'clock in the morning. He has finally fallen asleep. He asked after you, and whether you know what's happened to us. I told him that you know, and you feel for us, and that you wanted to come but your parents are preventing you. He took my hand, looked at me for a while and –

Joseph, have you ever seen a father cry? It's one thing to see a mother cry, but when a father weeps . . .

I can't write anymore. Too many tears.

Your Judith

26.   *July 29, 1904*

Yes, it is very bad. But I can't escape these woes and leave them to others.

You want me to tell you what you can do for me? Oh, Joseph, you undertake more than you can perform: Can you bring back our robbed and ruined fortune? Can you make my father healthy again? Or can you make it so you are always at my side? No, you can't, Joseph. You can't.

You tell me to come to you. You think your parents

would like me. That's very nice. You settled on a plan, because you think the plan will bring me to you sooner than anything else. In my heart, I'm willing to do as you say, but it has to wait. Let my father's health improve, and I won't dwell on what kind of reception I'll have from your parents. I will only think about you, and about our happiness together. When I think of your plan, all I see in it is *you*, and it's enough that I know that it means that I can be with you.

Your Judith

27.   *July 31, 1904*

I cried, Joseph, when I read your letter, but at the same time it also consoled me. How you suffer because you love me so. Darling, how I long to fly to you and assuage your suffering! But do not ask me to come now. Until my father is well again, I cannot leave this house, however much my heart yearns for you. I must not, I cannot!

The rabbi came today to perform the mitzvah of visiting the sick. He updated my father's will and comforted him by saying that at the end of his 120 years, he would be in a position to write a more substantive document. My father only gestured dismissively with his hand and turned his face to the wall. The rabbi asked if certain people (not ones you know) had repaid their debts to us. My father responded, "Those are old debts. Sometimes they are repaid to the widow after a man dies. If they pay her, they will receive my thanks from the world to come."

"Don't talk like that. You will live in this world, with your family. You have children to care for."

"They will be taken care of."

"Place your hope in the Eternal One that you might live. Everything is in His hands."

"Who knows in whose hands we lie. I've given up on the idea!"

"Don't talk that way. It's sinful."

My father sighed and looked around as though he were searching for someone. I went to him and straightened his pillows. The rabbi said his goodbyes and left.

"Did you hear, Judith?" my father asked. "How can I rebuild from nothing when my years of hard work have been ruined? . . . Are you crying? And you haven't slept at all? You are so pale."

He held my face in his hands and looked deep into my eyes as though he were reading my fortune and seeing my future. Tears welled up in his eyes.

It was more than I could bear. I buried my face in his pillow. Our tears mingled.

Forgive me, Joseph. Forgive –

Your Judith

28.   *August 8, 1904*

It's been eight days since I wrote to you last.

You must know by now that my father died eight days ago from an inflammation of the brain. Aaron wrote you everything. Everything? No. The deepest despair is buried where no one can see it. Tears flow more freely when there is no one here to count them.

I turn my eyes to where he lay, and it pains me to think that I didn't show him how much I loved him while he was still alive.

The day before his death he asked me again about you. I told him how in love we are, and how happy I would be when he was well again and you would come to be with me. He gave me his blessing. How holy he looked –

I cannot write any more, Joseph. You are alive and yet I am drawn to the place where he lay. I will sit there and think about death.

                                        Your Judith

29.   *August 15, 1904*

Dear Joseph, logic speaks to the head, and not to the heart. He is dead. He died. We live and we should act for our own sake. But what should we do? All my mother does is one thing: she cries. I cannot comfort her. She would see my efforts as an insult to the memory of our dear departed. She is beyond consolation. We have to let her cry. She is too weak to hold back so much sorrow.

How full of life you are! How lovely your dreams are!

I read what you wrote over and over again, Joseph. I will go with you, all you have to do is say where. Where exactly is your "far, far away?"

Your Judith

30.   *August 20, 1904*

My dear Joseph! How happy your letter made me! The steamship ticket arrived yesterday but I didn't want to write to you about it until I heard from you where you want to take me, where your "far, far away" is. I could hardly read your letter, I was so anxious to know where you were leading me. And now I know that you want this for me, for us all. How good and sympathetic you are, Joseph!

My aunt writes that I should leave as soon as possible and ask for my father's blessing as I go. My mother cried. How unhappy she is! If I had only had your letter then, I could have comforted her by telling her that you were coming to be with me, and that you would be going with me to America! Joseph, my dear, I will leave off writing for now. I can hear my mother reading Job with heart-breaking sobs. I will tell her my happy news, I mustn't keep it to myself.

Your Judith

31.   *August 24, 1904*

Yes, yes, we will love each other as no two have ever loved in the history of the world. We will be happy and proud and independent. We will teach others to love and to believe in love. Everything that you write, Joseph, is so dear to me. Your hopes are mine. I see everything through your eyes now, and everything seems good.

While you were in jail I was afraid that you would be drawn away and ride off to join the radicals. Now I have nothing to fear. You are mine. All mine! I would have fought even against the "better half of humanity" if it would have sacrificed you for the sake of its peasants. We have our own sacrificial altar!

So, we are going, Joseph. On Tuesday, at ten o'clock in the evening we will meet at the Wachman Brothers! You know, Joseph, I am so afraid. If you weren't under police surveillance I would say that we should try to obtain foreign passports. They're turning away so many people at the border.

Now I have to start to say my goodbyes, and then, Joseph, I will go to you. To *you*, with my whole life, my whole soul . . .

Your Judith

32.   *August 31, 1904*

Joseph, I am here, on the other side of the border. I stare in the direction from which you should be coming. They say that you will come with the next party. I want to go back, to be by your side, but they won't let me. They don't want to risk smuggling the same head over the border two times.

Joseph, Joseph, my heart dies here, waiting for you . . .

I hope that the person who takes you this letter will return with you in one piece.

Your Judith

33.   *August 31, 1904, in the evening*

Joseph, the second party arrived without you and without the messenger I'd entrusted with my earlier letter. They say that you will come in the morning with the third party. They are very upset. I can't get anything more out of them about you. They speak in broken, incomprehensible words, or they don't say anything at all. On *Shabes* the ship will be here. They say we have to prepare for the ship. We can't lose any more time waiting here. What should I do? What can I do?

I stand here looking for you and waiting for you to come.

Your Judith

34.   *September 2, 1904*

I am in B_____. The ship departs today. They want to add me to the ship's register along with all the others who are traveling, but I refuse to go without you. The Wachmans promised me that you would be here soon. If only I could believe them with as little worry as they utter these words! I ask them and they just look at me, don't respond, and answer someone else. They reassure me that no harm came to you back there, amidst all the chaos and the sounds of shots being fired. (Who knows what they mean by "nothing bad"?). They say that you were just stopped at the border and turned back. Back? To where? They don't say.

I'm sending this letter to be forwarded to you through the Wachmans. Write back as soon as you can. You know the address.

The innkeeper told me that if I stay here to wait for another ship, I'll have to pay for it on my own because I'm staying for personal reasons. I will stay here and wait for you. I can't go without you.

Your Judith

35.   *September 4, 1904*

I just received a letter from your home. It came via the Wachman Brothers. I don't understand what you wrote. Are you more angry that you were turned away at the border, or that I didn't let you cross the boundaries of love when we were together in the Wachmans' house? You write, "Everyone at the inn regarded you as my wife, but you behaved toward me like a stranger . . ." *Like a stranger*, Joseph! You were intoxicated with passion, but I remained sober. When I saw the way you suddenly became like *another man*, it was that man that I repelled.

You understood. You grew pale, you shook and trembled and tried to hide your face from me. It was then that I wanted to kiss your hand, fall at your feet, die for you!

Did I hurt you, Joseph? Oh, tell me that I didn't! I know myself to be innocent, and yet forgive me. Forgive.

I wait impatiently for you to come. How long will I have to wait here? How terribly slowly time passes here! But the comfort of knowing I'm not waiting in vain gives me the strength to carry on.

Your Judith

36.   *September 7, 1904*

Joseph, a stormy wind blows between the lines of the letter I received from you today. Did my "coldness" toward you really cause you so much pain? Can you really believe that I don't love you as much as you love me? That I don't trust you?

Joseph, believe me when I say that I'm not disposed toward debating you now about the "impassioned embrangling of two souls in love," and "how those who love passionately can forget about the rest of the world."

I offer you no apologies. You can compare me, if you want, to my mother or my grandmother. They were also "indifferent" women. They didn't lose their way, they didn't pursue the pleasures of the moment. But their love was true, it was lifelong devotion. Would you rather that I was like other, more "modern" women?

I no longer believe you are coming here. Unfortunately, there are some borders that you simply aren't capable of crossing. If I stop and ask myself: What will the future hold? I feel, and my heart does not lie, that your misgivings have returned; you've become afraid to take any risks in life.

The week will soon be over and my finances can't hold out much longer. I can't afford to wait here for your "perhaps," "maybe," and "possibly." I don't think you even believe yourself when you say that you will make the journey with me. Should I go back home? You don't write anything about that. Your silence suggests that one way or the other, I will have to go on this journey. Yes, I have my mother and the children to provide for.

Oh, Joseph, if you knew how my heart aches! How I despair without you! And who knows how long we will be parted! My heart trembles, but fate drives me on this long path, alone and friendless.

Your Judith

37.   *September 9, 1904*

My ship will soon depart. My belongings are already on board, my name is listed on the manifest alongside those of other passengers. I am going.

I look at the locket with your picture on it that you gave me on that happy-unfortunate evening in the inn. The little diamond on the gold cover looks like a lonely star to me. I look at your picture. I feel the lack of you. You should have been here.

The few words that just I received from you, written, it appears, when you were in an agitated state, are not enough to divert me from my purpose or duty to my family. Going to you would have meant leaving their fortune up to chance. And after all you are still subject to your parents' whims.

I am going now and will wait for you there. Do not despair. We will slowly, but surely, span the bridge to our happiness.

Not long ago I was feeling so weak and helpless. Now I feel an unfamiliar strength growing inside of me. I believe, Joseph, that I will be strong enough to do what I must, what my fate requires of me.

I kiss your picture in the locket. I will wear it over my heart. And I carry you *in* my heart.

38.   NEW YORK
                                              October 5, 1904

My dear Joseph!

I have just arrived. In between greeting and embracing my relatives, I write these few lines to you. After a stormy passage, and after undergoing the stringent immigration examinations, I came out whole and unscathed.

I was expecting to have a letter from you waiting for me here. It will surely arrive tomorrow, or the next day. When I receive it I will write more. For now, I am very tired.

I did find two letters from home waiting for me here. *They* write about how they miss me,

                                              Your Judith

39.

I received your letter today. I read it three times. I wanted to make it last. Yes, I know that when your heart aches because the one dearest to you has gone away, it is hard to write. Your pen falls from your hand, your thoughts are carried away in the direction of your beloved, but rarely reach their intended destination. If only there was such a thing as a telegraph for thoughts.

The whole of my journey I was thinking only of you. I almost felt that you were there beside me.

I avoided making the acquaintance of others. I wanted to be alone. The laughter and songs that surrounded me only made me feel more lonely and desolate.

One of the passengers traveling with me caught my attention by speaking about love. He had been disappointed in love before and dismissed the idea of true love, calling it nothing more than motion sickness. What he said irritated me. He seemed to me like a messenger from evil spirits sent to persecute those with hearts that believed and held onto love.

The journey seemed uncomfortably long to me. You weren't there with me.

My uncle and aunt were very welcoming. My aunt cried with joy. I remind her of her home, her youth, and my mother.

I am already dressed in American clothes. My shoes are still a greenhorn's shoes, but who looks at shoes?

Here, I have a cousin Benny, a cousin Mike, a cousin Jessie who has many gold teeth, and a cousin Sadie, a very noisy girl. They all speak English and a broken Yiddish.

They gave me my own room. The window looks out onto the grey wall of a six or seven story building. We live on the second floor. In my room there is a large bed, a small table and two chairs. I am sitting on one of the chairs now, writing you this letter. My heart yearns for you. How far away we are from each other now!

Joseph, you will not have to wait before receiving an answer to your letters. *I* will expect a letter from *you* every day. *Every day*. And if one evades me today, or tomorrow, then I will wait until the next day for it.

Your Judith

40.

A feeling, an exhaustion from feeling too much, sweeps over me and tries to free itself from control of my thoughts. One thought follows another, crashing into one another and shattering.

Should I send you the shards of my thoughts? But then I didn't find many whole thoughts in your letter either. You write that "my spirit will be close to you." Oh, Joseph, why are we fooling ourselves? I don't have you, and it's me that you want, not my spirit. I've thought about it over and over again and I have made some semblance of peace with it. I used to think of you as some kind of a god, but once I compared you with other people I came to see that you are more of a man than I understood before.

Yes, it isn't your fault that you were created with such a passionate nature, that you forget about the angelic nature of love, and are only interested in its human component.

What can I do to show you how much I love you? This is a matter of belief, of feeling. There was a time when we understood each other implicitly, when you could read in my eyes what I felt about you.

Joseph, it's so hard for me. My heart aches. It pains

me. But no, I don't want my letter to end in tears. I know that you can't bear it.

Your Judith

41.

When I took your letter from Jessie today, my heart was pounding. She laughed at her greenhorn cousin who spends too much time on 'letters.' "We don't waste our time on such foolishness, do we, Louie?" she said to her "friend." He is studying to be a doctor, and they're paying for it. They are getting a doctor on installments, and when he finishes he will be obliged to marry her.

"Really, you receive so many letters. Who are they from, I wonder . . ." he asked.

"They are from the kind of people who like to write often." I answered.

I went off to be by myself. I read your letter and I felt strangely grateful for everything:

For my uncle, who says every time he sees me that I am a pretty girl and I should find myself a wealthy husband.

For my aunt, who never ceases to bemoan that I am a poor orphan, and who helped me find work so quickly (in America everyone works) and who will allow me to pay for everything she gives me, as I insist.

For Jessie, who doesn't want to introduce me to her friends until I learn English. It will take me a long time to know English well, she says. Her "friend" says otherwise.

For Mike, who cries and complains right under my window when I'm trying to write or think.

For Sadie who laughs at my greenhorn shoes and who shows me how people in America walk, stand, sit, talk, open and shut their mouths.

And I am especially grateful for you—I saved you for last. You know that "the last evening is the loveliest." I am grateful that you had the help of your friends to cheer you up. Too much yearning will cost you your health. I know that Ana Andreyevna doesn't understand why anyone would ever want to leave Russia. But at least *you* understand . . . And why shouldn't you tell her that I am the one pulling you away from that field of holy endeavor where you were once so happy? Russian students can be so high-spirited, they are more lively than Jews.

Be well and be happy. Maybe I won't write any more until I receive your answer to my letter. You're probably grateful to hear that.

Your Judith

42.   NEW YORK
                                      November 9, 1904

Yes, I am glad that you are content to know that somewhere far away, on the other side of the ocean, a heart
beats for you. You anticipate and read my love letters
that call out to you and draw you toward me. But do you
know what I decided today? I won't "tempt you with
love from afar" anymore. From now on, I will only write
letters in response to yours, even if it takes you a month
or more to write to me. Why should it matter? My heart
tells me that it may take longer than a month for you to
write.

You write that someday you will come to your dear
one, even for one moment of joy. Just so you can know
that, "I was happy once, even if only for a moment."

For one moment I would not advise you to undertake
the journey. Your dear one is more exacting than that,
she wants many, many happy moments, and she wants
them without delay.

I didn't write to you about the storm we encountered
in the ocean, not because I didn't want to scare you
off. Don't I know that you could weather the storm, as
I did? The storm on the ocean I think, was no greater
than the storm inside of me, in my sea of emotions. The
first storm, which was written up in the newspapers, has

long ago passed. I've written to you already something of the second storm, its sister.

My work in the silk blouse factory is going fairly well, but I wish I was earning more money. Do you see how materialistic I've become?

Send my regards to your little sister. I hope that she is feeling better. It was kind that your friend came to sit with her for an evening.

Be well and happy.

Your Judith

PS: I will inquire for you about what life is like here for intellectuals.

43. *November 15, 1904*

Maybe it's true that your parents are unkind. They are disagreeable. But I don't trust your new friends either.

Joseph, your trust in them impels me to do something I ordinarily would not: Do you know which one of your friends could have sent me these lines?

"Some men love to take on new ideas and ideologies. You can never trust such a man's love. It's better to swear it off. Men like that forget those who are far away and only love those who are close at hand."

I don't trust or have respect for anonymous letters, but I think you had better find out who is the man—or woman—who got my address from you and represented you to me in such a bad light.

Your Judith

44.   NEW YORK
                                    November 20, 1904

Perhaps you are right, Joseph, that I still don't know you very well. But whose fault is it—mine, for not knowing you well? Or yours, for not making yourself better known?

You are so good for wanting to come here for my sake. But you must know that your "for your sake" both cheers me, on the one hand, and insults me on the other. For my sake—and not for yours? Doesn't being here matter at all to you, for *your own sake*?

But enough about that. I'd rather tell you my news: I now have a better position than before and I'm earning twice as much money.

Today I'm sending Misha money for a warm winter coat and boots. My mother is afraid he'll catch cold, and he seems to share the concern. He asks too often if it's as cold in America as it is at home. He also asks what a person like him can do here, whether he'll have to study first or if he'll be able to go right to work.

Berman is thinking of going to Palestine. Heniya is also interested in going. Rokhl and Shimka are learning to operate a sewing machine and studying English. I send them books to help them learn.

What else can I tell you? It's already midnight, and I have to get up at seven.

Be well, and write more often.

Your Judith

45.   NEW YORK
December 11, 1904

My love! Only just now you have made the discovery that we are growing apart, and that I love myself much too much! But you say you also love me too much. So at least we have this in common.

But enough about myself. I will answer your questions about our intellectuals here in America. You seem to be so keenly interested. How very practical of you.

There aren't as many private tutors here as there are at home. Education here is free, both in the elementary schools and in the institutions of higher learning. The Russian-Jewish youth who study distinguish themselves here in many ways. In comparison with them, the

American-born students only excel when it comes to sports.

Evidently, your friends seem to have a grudge against America, since they write you such bad things about it. They must have placed too many hopes on it, they expected too much. They feel disappointed. It's true, many intellectuals here face adversity: some of them are simply not suited to life here, others can't adjust to the working conditions, and so on. But the devil is not as terrifying as they describe. Unless they miss the spiritual unrest they faced at home. If they truly sought a spiritual life and intellectual work, they would have no cause for complaint.

No, my love, it's not so hopeless here.

Your Judith

46.   NEW YORK
                                          January 5, 1905

Today marks three months since I first came to New York.

It's been two weeks since your last letter—fourteen days, three hundred thirty six hours, every hour consisting of sixty minutes, every minute . . . What's the point of such an accounting?

Joseph, why did you ask me whether you should come here or not? I took you to be so much stronger than you are!

Joseph, I must tell you that all the things you did not describe in your letters to me I read about anyway in my mother's letters. Your aunt and Aaron told her that they will soon attend the wedding of a wealthy couple in your townThey asked my mother what kind of a present they should bring you.

Now I understand what you meant when you said, "dreams and reality, desire and life, longing and circumstances ..."

Perhaps "damned nature" will make fewer "unhappy circumstances" in your life than you will encounter in the "damned land of dollars"? Who knows what true happiness is? It used to be that you thought that you found happiness with me. But what kind of happiness could you have with me? I can't give you any more than my heart and soul.

I promised myself that I wouldn't beg you to come here and I *will not.* Your heart will tell you what to do.

Judith

PS: Should Aaron have been the one to write a letter announcing your wedding? There's no reason to suspect him

of doing it out of ill will. Or maybe there is? Oh, it's not
worth even talking about it. Judith

47.   NEW YORK
                                          January 20, 1905

You have forgotten me, and I will forget all about you.
Everything is fine. You can keep on asking me for my
advice and then doing just what your father and mother
dictate. I won't stand in your way. I don't care. It doesn't
bother me in the least that you're getting married to that
wealthy woman. No other reason for our parting ways
would have made circumstances easier than this one.
My God, you're selling yourself for money! I'm not jealous of—money.

As I write this letter, I'm thinking that I might . . . But,
no, I won't do anything. Nothing. Why should I, if it's
nothing to me? I am not at all concerned. The woman
at your uncle's pharmacy told my mother that "it's such
a joy." Very nice. You should be happy. Yes, joy soon runs
out for the poor. It lingers a little longer for the rich.

                                          Judith

48.   NEW YORK
                                               March 5, 1905

They exaggerate the danger. All that happened is that I caught cold. It happened one time when I went to send off a letter.

I refuse to write how I feel. I want everyone to leave me alone about my feelings.

The climate here is not detrimental to me.

Believe me, I will not be using the address of your famous Russian physician. I have sufficient confidence in my American doctor.

J. Lilien

49.   NEW YORK
                                               April 6, 1905

I don't see why it would make any difference in the progress of my illness to know just which letter I was sending when I caught cold.

What possible use could these be, what good can they do me, and what bad? I don't expect anything from anyone and I won't complain.

J. Lilien

PS: Yes, it's possible that Berman would sooner immigrate to America than Palestine. You shouldn't laugh at him for it. Being adventuresome is one thing, but sometimes you have to take other things into account. I haven't yet inquired about what highfalutin intellectuals can do in America

50.   NEW YORK
                                            June 7, 1905

I read all the letters I receive. I don't see the use in writing long letters. I don't want to take a long time to write, I'd rather spare myself and those who receive my letters, painful scenes. I don't want to ruin the peace and comfort of a man who had every right to sell himself for the sake of some peace and comfort.

                                            J. Lilien

51.   NEW YORK
                                            July 6, 1905

There's no need for me to explain the tone of my writing, and why I'm not talking about "you" and "me" when writing at all is of no use.

   "You can hide love, you can hide hate, but you can't hide your indifference."

   Yes, it's true. I'm entirely indifferent.

                                            J. Lilien

52.

Has it been six months since I last wrote? I didn't count them. Being free must truly be good, since you write about it with such joy.

I can't say how good it is. Only those who have sought to free themselves, and who know what to do with their freedom, would know.

J. Lilien

53.

Yes, you're right. Playing at love like that would cost us too much. I will write and let you speak for yourself. Forgive me for not having wanted to hear what you had to say. Why didn't you write to me yourself about all of this? Why didn't you try to convince me otherwise, if others were writing lies about you to me? I know you must have been prevented by the same bitter stubbornness that caused me to refuse to hear you out.

Is it true the doctors told you to leave the city? Your nerves were ruined from too much studying and you lay sick, my mother tells me, in our house, in my room, and you talked in your feverish haze, about whether you would come to me or not, about trying to cross the border, and you called out my name again and again. Poor Joseph! My mother thinks that something must have happened between us . . .

Misha writes: "Judith, I wish you were here, now that Joseph is with us. You don't even ask after him. He read your letter and turned his face to the wall. I think he cried. He was clearly upset that you didn't ask after him.

"He is so good to me. He kisses me and wants me to call him Yoysef, not Joseph.

"We went to our father's grave. He looked at it a long time in silence, just like you would. He held his face in his hands and I could see tears trickling through his fingers. I remembered how our father died, how you went away, and I burst into tears. He held me, and begged me not to cry, even as he was crying too.

"We were caught in a rainstorm. Mother was afraid we'd catch cold. I didn't catch cold but apparently Joseph did."

You see, Joseph, that Misha's letter made a stronger impression on me than yours did.

Today I am sending steamship tickets for Heniya and Misha (I'll send for my mother, Rokhl and Shimke later).

Heniya writes that she is very glad that you came to us (since she gave Berman her promise of marriage, she has been writing with many insinuations). She's also glad that you are so close with Berman. She says she knows why: It's because Berman plans to go to America to be with her.

Be well, Joseph. Take with this letter my assurances that I am not sending it out of pity but out of my love for you, which has not been extinguished and never will be.

Your Judith

54.

No, Joseph, your heart is not playing a trick on you. When you receive this letter, you should already have received, a week earlier, my letter that answers this question. By now you must already be convinced that I am not just taking pity on you or sending you the crumbs of my affection.

I understand your impatience for my answer. Time passes so slowly when you are waiting, and you wrote in the meantime.

You write: If I have not yet responded to you, you beg me to do it soon. You say I will not regret it.

But Joseph, it was only a moment after I sent my answer to you that I started to regret it. A nagging feeling settled upon my heart, and it seemed to me that answering you with kindness only was preparing me for disappointment later. I hope I won't feel like that again.

How I long to be there with you among the thick trees, the narrow lanes, the paths that we walked together!

There is no springtime here. The rays of the sun are blinding, and all I can see is the shine of the electric lights. I don't hear the sound of birds, only the rumbling of machines. With my eyes closed, in my memory I can relive what you are experiencing with your eyes open.

You love me. Not a moment has gone by, you write, that you weren't thinking of me, and you always said to yourself, "She doesn't love me, so I shouldn't love her." Joseph, you're right when you say, "the mouth can talk, but the heart goes on loving." I also used to tell myself not to love you but all the while my heart was faithful. True love won't be fooled, and if you're sure of your love, all you can do is love even more.

Your Judith

55.   NEW YORK
                                                    June 14, 1906

Today was an awful day. There's no breeze, the heat is suffocating, everything is withering. The air is leaden. It's so hot! People are dying of heat and hunger.

My thoughts slowly carry me to my home town, to my house, that you will soon be leaving.

Joseph, don't go away from us! Why are you in such a hurry to go? Misha writes that you said that you have a massive amount of work waiting for you at home. You don't want to sit empty-handed. You have to go.

A massive amount of work—work for the masses. Yes, you are drawn to the fray. Will you serve *our* people, or will you help the poor peasants achieve freedom?

I read about what's happening in Russia with fear and amazement. They shout, "Freedom, light!" and at the same time, "Beat the Jews, give them a good pounding!" On the one side there's an uprising of the peasantry, but on the other side there's a recruiting drive for peasant-driven oppression.

Are you really going away from us? You seem so much closer to me when I'm writing to you in our home!

No, I won't write to you about how I felt the whole time we were having a "spat." What would be the point? I'm glad it's over. Now, I focus on the present, which I, like you, think of as a waiting room for the future. A present moment in which I keep on living for what is to come . . . What will come?

Believe me, I don't ask this in vain. I'm sick of sailing without a sign of dry land. I am asking you because you aren't asking. I know you don't like to remain anchored in one spot.

Your Judith

56.   NEW YORK
June 22, 1906

I gaze at your latest letter, which you wrote from our house, in my room, and I'm overcome with longing. I picture you sitting there and writing, your head bent over the letter, your pen making rapid movements across the paper. You write and write all that you feel, barely taking the time to think . . .

"My pride, my joy, my bride—I will come to you and look into your eyes again, and see in them your whole pure, good soul. Oh, perhaps I shall be overpowered by such joy. I will fall dead at your feet."

Dead? How often that word came to my mind when I thought about my undying love for you! Love is death.

You ask if you were right to tell my mother about our happiness. I don't know. I can hardly imagine her reaction to your telling her our news. I only know that now she will worry even more about me, and she will suffer if we aren't able to be together soon. The older generation is more concerned with "letting things go too long." She'll start asking me questions, and she'll begin to suspect that we don't know how to answer them.

But you are happy, and I don't want to darken the bright sky of your joy with the lament that my heart can't help but sing out. I don't know what's the matter with me! I feel that if only you were still living at my house I wouldn't feel this way. I'm so strange. Why should it matter to me if you are at our house or not? Either way, you're not with me. And yet, it feels to me that when you left my home, you left me once again.

Misha writes that you promised you would write to him. He is very proud.

Everyone writes about you with love. They all love you, and I love you most of all.

Your Judith

57. NEW YORK
July 1, 1906

Now you are in your home, stripped by your parents of your free will. Joseph, I think if it weren't for them, you, yourself might be suppressing your own free will.

I understand what is happening all around you. I'm not ashamed to say that if I were with you, I would be on your parents' side in this. Not because of any love for them, but because I worry for you, for associating so closely with those kinds of people.

You must already know the opinion I have of those people, who, on the first night you arrived home after being at my house, came to you, demanded of you "the debt you owe humanity" and dragged you into their camp.

Ana Andreyevna said: "For the sake of humanity!" and she might as well have said, "For the sake of all that's good and worthy of love," but do you think that this "humanity" includes us, Jews? No! Her "humanity" is a Russian one. Those are her words, but enough—you know what I think. If you don't agree, I'm sorry, but I cannot change my opinion and I will not join with such "company" that even your parents oppose. It is out of the question.

I don't want to write any more about them. Don't write to me anymore about *her* and her "humanity." I don't trust her and I don't want to hear about it.

Your Judith

58.

August 2, 1906

Joseph, what is happening with you? Why can't you write and tell me everything? Why are you leaving your parents? What are they keeping you from?

Your letter was poorly written. What are you truly drawn toward: the revolutionary struggle, or the revolutionists? Are you certain that you are following the right path?

You are alone, Joseph, alone like me, here, without you. Do you want to know my opinion? If, given the present circumstances it seems impossible for you to come to me–then I will go to you! You were wrong to think that I would never go back on my decision to stay here. For you—I would! It would be as much for my own sake as it would be for yours.

I want to go to you. I feel that you must have someone at your side, someone who knows what you are feeling, who understands your thoughts, who shares your desires. I want to be that person for you–I want to be *the only one for you*!

I won't write any more today. Don't let other subjects crowd out this important decision: *I am coming*! I will come to you, if you want me to.

I await your answer. I will wait all month if I have to.

Your Judith

59.

September 1, 1906

I finally received your answer, if asking a question counts as an answer:

Why am I on your parents' side?

Am I motivated by anything other than anti-terrorism when I call you away from the struggle?

Am I testing you by saying that I will come to be with you?

My dear Joseph, when did you stop understanding the intention behind my words? Do you really not believe that I mean them in earnest? Do you doubt that I can love you as much as I do? You accuse me of writing as I did out of jealousy.

Who should I be jealous of, Joseph? Tell me, my love! Tell me everything that is going on with you there. Explain what your life is like, tell me about your work, your thoughts and feelings. Don't force me to try to interpret between the lines of your words, drawing too many rash conclusions, as you claim I do.

Your Judith

60.   *September 15, 1906*

I am writing to you this time not in response to your letter, but because of a letter I received from home. There was almost nothing to dwell on in your letter, other than to wonder why you didn't mention in it "humanity" or "the old regime" or the "new epoch," or all the other things you're supposed to be thinking of.

I was not pleased with your words about my heavenly goodness or the especially elevated tone of your letter. That's the tone I used to take with others when I had something to feel guilty about.

My mother asks me in her letter, "What is going to happen?" How can I answer her?

Heniya, Berman, and Misha are getting ready to come

here. They write that Aaron will also be coming soon. Things have gotten ugly for him in Russia. Soon I will see them, talk to them face to face. We will talk about you. But what will we say? I won't ask them anything. I don't want to learn from other people the things that you're not willing to write yourself.

I will write and tell my mother that it's my fault that you aren't set on coming here. I don't want her to be angry at you for not keeping your word. But how is it my fault? I'll have to come up with some kind of excuse. I will tell her that I don't love you that much, that I shouldn't have agreed so easily to be–

Your Judith

61.   *October 23, 1906*

Joseph, come to me! Give up your fight! It's not yours to fight. You will be lost. I ask you, for the sake of our love, to value your life and not sacrifice our happiness—yours and mine—so easily.

Your letters are unclear, I'm losing the thread of what is happening in your life. Come! I can no longer endure your letters. I don't want to write to you anymore. Every stroke of my pen pierces my nerves. The black, dead letters poison my soul. Oh, I don't want any more letters!

Aaron came to see me today and stayed a long time. His presence was difficult for me: I felt he was hiding something from me. The last time he was with you he said that you had a nice time together, but instead of simply telling me about it, he started to talk in broken words, and he stopped himself mid-sentence. Why does he torture me like that?

And why, Joseph, do you write to me so often as "my friend"? "Friend," when I used to be "dearest" or "my love"? Do you remember what you told me once, when I said "let's be friends?"

> *I love the flames, but not the embers*
> *I don't suffer halves of things.*
> *I would rather the sun never shined and glowed*
> *That I never saw the moon*
> *That my whole life was only darkness*
> *Pitch black, a night without stars:*
> *If you won't give me all of your love,*
> *I'm not interested in your friendship!*[1]

So, Joseph, can't you give me all of your love?

Your Judith

---

1 From D. Frishman (Author's note)

62.   *October 25, 1906*

I can't sleep. As soon as I close my eyes I see horrible images. My heart begins to pound, my body is covered in a cold sweat and I feel a fever over my body.

I sit and write to you, maybe that way I will dispel these awful images.

I have been gazing at your picture for a long time. It seems to me that the expression in your eyes has changed. I try to concentrate all my thoughts and feelings on the original version of this pale copy.

If I want to remember something good, I turn to one of your letters, one from the past. You don't write the way you used to. And why is that? Am I different than I used to be? Do I love you less? Or . . .

Oh, how my heart is pounding. Dr. Louie says that I shouldn't get excited. But if you were to come here and I could finally press you close to my heart . . .

I have thought about your coming, and I found myself with a strangely unshakable faith that you will come. I feel—and this is a rare sort of feeling—that you are getting closer to me. I close my eyes and listen in the silence to the sound of your steps as you approach my bed. You spread my hair out on my pillow and bury your face in it, you kiss my hair and cry with joy. I throw my arms around your neck, pull you toward me, but then

I control myself and keep myself from kissing you, so that my face is open to you. My lips tremble, waiting for your kiss. You bend over me . . . and I wake up, my heart pounding.

It's broad daylight now, but the night sometimes is brighter than the light of day. What is the day to me? I sit and write to you and wait.

Your Judith

63.   *November 4, 1906*

You made a mistake! You sent me the wrong letter! Maybe you even did it on purpose. Maybe you didn't have enough courage to write the honest truth to your "good angel."

It happened! I am grateful for the accident—if mixing up the letters was indeed a mistake—that showed me the truth about the situation in which I find myself. Now I know everything. I won't wait anymore for you, and I won't write, or hope, or believe anything! That was before, and now it's over. Everything between us is over.

Judith

64.
NEW YORK
March 2, 1907

Mr. Goldshmidt:

You sent me three letters, it's true. I was not able to answer them. Thank you for your inquiry. There is no reason for concern. My friends are making a fuss over nothing. It's possible the blood is coming from my throat, and not from my lungs.

Misha also told me that you wrote to him. Why did he respond as he did? He must not have known any better. How does he know, there, how I'm feeling here?

I don't lack anything. I don't need anything. I work and earn enough money to support myself and others.

J. Lilien

65.
NEW YORK
April 8, 1907

I enclose your letter of credit which I just received. I return it at once so that it may not become contaminated by my sputum.

J. Lilien

PS: Send me back my letters. My picture too.

66.   NEW YORK
                                                       May 15, 1907

Your last letter surprised me. You write that with my request for you to return my letters and picture, I erect a barrier between us. Is there not a barrier there already?

I don't want to ask you again, but I also don't intend on sending you any more letters.

                                                            J. Lilien

67.   NEW YORK
                                                    September 21, 1907

You ask me to stay friends and want to be sure that I will not refuse you. But why would I give you my friendship? You want to "win back your own self-respect"—have you lost it?

I see no reason not to honor your wish, and so I send you a greeting in friendship,

                                                            J. Lilien

68.

To my esteemed friend, Mr. Goldshmidt:

If you insist on thanking me so heartily for my friendship, then I will withdraw it. If it were even half as difficult as you think it was to agree to be your friend, I would not have done it. Rest assured that I am not diminishing the greatness of my deed only for the purposes of making it seem smaller to you.

I am not inclined to immerse myself in strangers' concerns, nor can I, as others do, see the quelling of the Russian revolution as the downfall of all of humanity and the final blow to the Jewish situation. I never believed that the success of the revolution would bring with it a culminating solution to the Jewish question.

My mother, sisters, and Misha are on their way to America. I sent them money for the voyage and they collected a few old debts. My mother writes, "An old debt is still a debt. Whoever is owed something must receive it, sooner or later."

You think it's no good that Misha grew up without a father and without a tutor?

If so, then what were we supposed to do? His father is dead, and a tutor costs money.

Your friend,
J. Lilien

69.   NEW YORK
                                          November 5, 1907

You write that it would make you glad to know that I am
happy.

I believe that it is time to tell you that I *am* happy. I
will tell you honestly. I met someone who has brought
much quiet joy to my life. He came at the right time, as
though I were expecting him.

I am so happy that I can make you happier by telling
you of my joy.

I have to end my letter here, because *he* will be here
any minute. I will write more another time.

                                          Your friend,
                                          J. Lilien

70.   NEW YORK
                                          December 6, 1907

My mother, my sisters, and my beloved Misha are here!
We have rented a lovely apartment. Rokhl is already
working in the same shop where I am now in charge.
Shimka will study and help my mother around the
house, Misha will go to school. In the meantime I'm trying to teach him a little. Oh, what a dear little tease he is!

He throws his book aside and grabs me and showers me with kisses! He is a delight.

Why are you so surprised about my unexpected happiness? Am I sure that he loves me? Yes, I am sure, very sure. He has spoken to me at length about my work. He earns enough for the both of us—he works in a bank—but I don't want to live off someone else's earnings. There will be time enough later for that.

If it's a sin to concentrate all of my finest feelings on one person, then I am a sinner, and so is he. We love each other and we forget that a "humanity" exists somewhere in Russia. We want to *live*, we don't want to cry. We want to be so happy that we can later say in truth that, "We were happy."

You must excuse me for writing so much about my own personal happiness. I would never consider doing so if I didn't know that I was sharing it with someone who was also happy. No, no matter what you say, the world is not such a bad place, and happiness is not so rare to come by.

We are all going to the theater tonight. I must hurry to finish off this letter. Otherwise I would write more. Yes, I now have so much to write about.

Your friend,
J. Lilien

71.   NEW YORK
                                January 5, 1908

You shouldn't believe everything that whoever it was who wrote to you said. And I don't have to confirm or deny it. Aaron probably wanted to be agreeable and wrote a lot, as you asked him to. So he wrote, and whatever he didn't already know, he guessed at, adding his own embellishments.

You shouldn't be surprised that Aaron sees me as an unhappy woman. I didn't tell him about my good fortune. I don't like to proclaim it in public.

It's true that I said in the past that it's only possible to love once in your life. I was so inexperienced then.

You ask so many questions, and I have to say that you are overstepping in what you expect from me, your *friend.* I don't want to answer many of them, nor do I want to respond to Aaron's gossip about me.

I'll answer one question: I didn't ask him about his past and he didn't ask me about mine. I believe him, when he says that he has never loved anyone but me. That's enough for me.

                                Your friend,
                                J. Lilien

72.

I can hardly recognize you between your last letter and this one. In your last letter you had so much to say about happiness—and this time you hardly have anything to say at all. "Life is nothing more than a lie. Everything changes until you can hardly recognize it at all."

How did you come to be so lonely? Your decision to leave everyone, to withdraw into yourself, to be alone, entirely alone, is achievable, but it won't last long because it's too easily accomplished. Having something to fight for is a different matter entirely.

So give loneliness a try. Loneliness can be useful sometimes. When you are alone, you understand yourself better, you find yourself.

With sympathy for your pessimistic mood and your closer self-acquaintance, I remain your friend,

J. Lilien

73.

Don't worry. I understood what you told me about your pessimism as you intended me to: such moods come and go.

You imagine that I am alone, and you miss me. I ask you, why should you want me, of all people?

You ask, does he fill up my whole world? Does he fulfill my every desire? What desire? All I want is for him to have the desire to fulfill my desires . . .

He sees nothing wrong with my writing to you. He's not concerned. But I'm not interested in writing more often or writing more. I prefer to spend my time reading, going for walks, and conversing.

With sympathy, now, for your more optimistic mood,

Your friend,
J. Lilien

74.   NEW YORK
May 10, 1908

Mr. Goldshmidt:

I have sympathy for you, and also for her. You are so certain and she . . . she . . . but it isn't her fault that there are so many "lovely and good" men in the world and she wants to give each some of her love. You don't know how frivolous girls can be!

You have my full sympathy for your present sorrow,

J. Lilien

75.

My friend, Goldshmidt:

I received your three letters. Although you write so often, I still don't want to meddle in the misunderstandings between the two of you.

Do you think it is possible, all of the sudden, for someone to feel so removed from someone who has been false to her, that it wouldn't even bother her when he belongs to someone else? Of course not! One can't stop loving so quickly, just because she fell in love—at least the kind of love she is capable of—with another. It's hard to understand.

I, too, have heard that the god of love is capricious. What then? Serve him faithfully and don't complain.

76.

You must forgive me that in response to your addressing me as your "best," "beloved," and "dearest friend" I respond only with "friend." Everyone has her own way of writing. If I don't like repeating those terms, you shouldn't judge me for it. I don't like to repeat what others say—I write my own mind.

How could I have known that you were talking about the capriciousness of the god of love, about the winter and summer, autumn and spring of a person's soul?

Whether or not I understand what you mean, I'm reading what you write, and you've said many times that is all that you want from me. What else do you want?

No, you and I were never officially engaged. I'm pleased that it was never official.

J. Lilien

77.

Has it already been a year since I agreed to be your friend? One year, and it seems that we have been friends so long. I hope that we will stay friends.

In your letter today you played too much with your words, even though you said words are often rebound to the speaker so hard and sharp that they plunge straight into the heart. Then protect your heart! Be content with friendship and don't try to put anything else in its place.

Friendship or nothing.

Your inappropriate expressions for ordinary, simple friendship have robbed me of my interest in writing to you for today.

J. Lilien

78.   *September 25, 1908*

Please, don't pour out your heart to me. If you think I'm
not capable of feeling, how can you possibly expect me
to sympathize with you? If you won't tell me everything,
how can I judge? And if I can't come to conclusions, how
could I accuse her of anything?

I don't know how significant her offense was, but you
shouldn't say that about her. She is your . . . your wife.
And if she wants your friendship, don't take it away from
her. Who knows what time will bring.

J. Lilien

79.   NEW YORK
October 1, 1908

I regret that I ever wrote to you about my happiness.
Why do *you* write about it so much? Why do you contin-
ually ask about it?

Who wrote and told you that I'm not happy? Who
was it?

As to your other questions, I can only say the following:

It is indeed possible to love more than once, but it's
impossible to trust someone more than once.

You can find everything where you lost it, except for
love.

Your friend,
J. Lilien

80.   NEW YORK
December 25, 1908

Yes, I made the whole thing up. It was a lie. I am not in love with anyone. I don't have anyone.

No one.

Why did I make it up?

I didn't want you to worry about my being unhappy. I wanted to get even with you, to show you that I was as happy as you were.

Don't you understand that your friendship was an insult to me? Your letter, in which you so freely wrote about everything, made me decide to try to fool you about my own situation, to fool you with an imaginary happiness, so I wrote to you and you believed me: You wanted to believe me, so you did.

It was hard to write the lie the first time; I almost decided to tear up the letter. I decided to make myself out to be your equal until you expressed your doubt. But when you wrote back you only provoked my desire to lie even further, and then it was as though the lie spoke for itself: I was a Khlestakov, playing my part.

And I didn't even regret it. The lie made you happy. It made it so you didn't have to punish yourself for my sadness and loneliness, for which you now must hold yourself responsible.

It's hard for me to write about this. I hope that you will understand and forgive your friend –

J. Lilien

81. NEW YORK
February 24, 1909

You write, "We loved each other too passionately to be able to forget it. We were caught up in our love the whole time, against our will."

Yes, we were caught up in our love for so long, that we were captured by it.

At the very least, I have been unable to forget any of it.

J Lilien

82. *April 13, 1909*

I didn't respond to your letter because I didn't want to write the same thing that I wrote in my last letter.

You want to come here, because you think that I am not telling you the truth about what's happening here. If you are so interested, I can tell you some news about us: Last week we moved to a better apartment, further away from the noise of the city. Our Heniya gave birth to a son two weeks ago. Berman is in seventh heaven.

We are busy this week getting ready for Rokhl's wedding with Aaron.

And soon we will have something else to celebrate: Our Shimka is marrying cousin Benny. His parent's aren't very happy with his choice: Benny is a lawyer, already out of law school, and he could have found a wife with a large dowry. But it will be alright. Here, in America, these kinds of obstacles can be overcome more easily than they were in Russia.

Misha's making progress in his studies. It's amazing how fast he learned English.

It gives me great satisfaction that I was able to bring them all here. You see, you can sometimes feel happier when you do something big for a few people than when you work to do something small for the masses. You said once that a person derives more joy in life when their fire burns for one person alone, than with countless sparks burning for all of humanity.

As for me, there's no cause for concern. The doctor says that I might get better, we just have to see.

Aaron was just here to see me. He brought me some eau-de-cologne from the pharmacy. I asked if he was getting tired of bringing me all of these different remedies.

"You think I would get tired of doing something for *you*?" he asked.

"You never would?"

"You won't need me forever."

"I hope not."

"Certainly not. You will be better soon."

"Either that, or I won't live forever."

"No one does."

"It's a shame that people have to die."

"You're talking about death as though it's a joke."

"Just like I talk about life. I would like to see what it's like in hell. It must be a happy place."

"They won't let you in there. You didn't sin."

Dr. Louie says that I sinned by not sinning. Sinning is living, and a person should be punished for not using the few opportunities they are given to live.

Does that mean that I never lived at all?

How sad, and how foolish.

J. Lilien

❖

83.   NEW YORK
                                              May 16, 1909

I was expecting your letter. Aaron told us that you were
coming. Come, our door is open to everyone. We will all
be at home. We will be happy to see you.

                                              Judith Lilien

84.   *May 23, 1909*[2]

It would have been better if you hadn't come to see us.
You would have been spared my cold reception, and I
would not have had to see what was once everything to
me, and now is nothing.

Your coming made everyone else feel that all was
right with you. You won everyone to your side. I have
almost no one anymore except for myself. But as long
as I have myself for support I wouldn't hide from you. I
greeted you with a smile.

No, my hand didn't quiver in yours, and my voice
didn't tremble. I heard it myself.

You have changed! Time washed away your delicate
features. The once-beautiful upturned corners of your

---

2 This note was found after her death, at her bedside.

mouth were turned down in an ill-humored grimace. But you are still attractive and handsome, and I was proud and also pained by your appearance.

You spoke about life, about joy and about the future. But how ashen you became when you looked deep into my eyes! What did you see in them that scared you so?

I won't see you again. Don't try to see me. Don't ask for more cold smiles. They don't bring either of us any pleasure. I am bitter, I know. But I can't be any other way.

It is too late . . .

I wouldn't have accepted Jessie's invitation if I had known that I would see you there. I know that it wasn't your fault. Jessie wanted to surprise us, so she invited both of us to be her guests. I didn't want to be sad but couldn't be happy. I shouldn't have, but I drank a glass of wine. My head started spinning. You took me by the arm and led me to a different room, where there was more air and less noise. When you started speaking to me in the half-darkness, talking like you used to, and you covered my lips with kisses—I didn't know what to do. My chest felt as if it would burst. I felt like I was choking. It was warm in my mouth. When your eyes pleaded with me for an answer, blood spurted out of my throat. You saw it, and you also saw that I felt pity for you.

You said that you doubted I ever loved you. "True love," you argued, "can forgive and forget everything." Yes, but are you the same Joseph that I loved once? Your doubt shows that you are not the same man. He knew how I loved him. But he didn't know how I suffered, he didn't concern himself with the pain of my wounded heart, he didn't heed my desperate pleas to come to me—because I tore up the letters that were dampened with my tears. Deep inside myself I carried my pain. Forlorn, despondent, I attended the funeral for my happiness.

I lie with my eyes closed and I see images from the past, by the inn near the border. He tells me about himself, about the prison. He mentions Anyuta's name. I tensely strain to listen to his voice. It doesn't waver, but I feel that he is hiding something.

"You know, I'd like to be someone else—a blonde girl, a carefree, singing girl who would flit like a butterfly to you, right next to your heart."

"You—someone else? And why do you need to be next to my heart, if you're already inside of it! You're the one I hold in my heart, you're the only one I want and no one else."

Inside me I was shouting in triumph as I threw myself into the arms of my one and only love, my dear one.

"Judith! You are mine!"

"Yours, Joseph, with all my heart and soul!"

"Do you love me, Judith?"

"Shh . . ." and I seal your lips with a passionate kiss.

"Say something, my love."

"I can't talk. Can you, Joseph?"

"No, Judith, I can't."

We are silent. I can hear his silence. It speaks to me of eternal love, loyalty, and joy.

A deep, hidden fear came over me that I would be completely torn away from you, so I kept up our correspondence. Each letter was a new disappointment. I thought I would answer you and agree to our friendship but you would never know how I suffered. And the more I loved you (*how I loved you!*) the more I guarded my words so not even a hint of it would sneak in and give me away.

I dreamed that I was dead. You all stood around me and mourned me. They led you to my grave and you stood under a black canopy. I wanted to cry out but I couldn't. I silently begged them to take you away, because you were not the same man that I loved, and I didn't want to break my life's pledge to him. You hid your face in your hands. Everyone looked at you and cried.

When I opened my eyes, two cold heavy tears fell from them—dead tears.

The day is ending. Soon the long dark night will begin. I will lie here and wait for death. In my imagination, I shall again see a dark, tall figure approaching my window. Who is it? Is it you? Or maybe it's death?

I want to see the sky. The high walls hide it from me. The sun begins to set. The sky is lit by a red sunset, and then my sun sinks down . . .

GLOSSARY

Chinovnik [Чиновник/*tshinovnik*]
An officeholder or bureaucrat serving in the civil or court service in tsarist Russia.

Gymnasium
A secondary school preparing students for higher education at a university.

Holofernes
In the Book of Judith, an Assyrian invading general who occupied countries surrounding Assyra and demanded that all the populations worship Nebudchadnezzar. In Holofernes' siege against Bethulia, Judith, a Hebrew widow, entered Holofernes's camp, seduced him, and then beheaded him while he was drunk, allowing the Hebrews to defeat their enemy.

Kamarinskaya [камаринская]
A traditional Russian folk dance.

Khlestakov [Хлестаков]
A central character in Nikolai Gogol's 1836 play "*The Government Inspector*" satirizing political corruption in tsarist Russia.

Kishinev

The Kishinev Pogrom of 1903 was an anti-Jewish riot that took place in Kishinev (now Chișinău, Moldova). In the violent outbreak, 49 Jews were killed,1,500 homes were damaged, and an unknown number of individuals were subject to violence and rape. The event received worldwide attention and acquired a symbolic status as the archetypical pogrom.

Melamed (מלמד)

A religious teacher.

Poalei-Tsiyon (פועלי-ציון/*poyle-tsien*)

A Labor Zionist organization merging revolutionary socialism with Jewish nationalism, stressing the notion that a territorial base in Palestine would redress Jewish economic and political marginality.

Shabes (שבת)

Judaism's day of rest on the seventh day of the week, ie. Saturday.

Zhidovka (жидовка)

A derogatory term for a Jewish woman.

Translator's Postface

AT THE TURN OF THE TWENTIETH CENTURY, Russia was roiling with political activity. Revolutionary ideas circulated not just among political theorists or lifelong revolutionaries, but as a part of the daily life and worldviews of people, especially young people, throughout imperial Russian society, even in the smallest towns.[1] Thousands of people found hope in the tenets of Marxism and Labor Zionism that they read in newspapers and literature illegally smuggled across the borders into Russia from radical emigre colonies. Amidst reactionary antisemitic violence and public accusations blaming Jews for political unrest, Jewish youth culture in Russia's Pale of Settlement

1 Faith Hillis quotes Russian Jewish socialist Grigorii Aronson as saying that in his Belarusian hometown at the turn of the century, "There was not a home completely free of illegal literature. There was not a family whose children did not participate in some kind of political circle." This Belarusian small town setting is precisely the context in which Miriam Karpilove's *Judith* takes place. See Grigorii Aronson, Revoliutsionnaia iunost': vospominaniia, 1903–1917 (New York: InterUniversity Project on the History of the Menshevik Movement 1961), quoted in Faith Hillis, *Utopia's Discontents: Russian Emigres and the Quest for Freedom, 1830s–1930s*. (Oxford University Press, 2021), 159.

was shot through with radical politics that empowered its participants to believe they could reshape their world.[2]

In the center of all this sits Judith, the protagonist of Miriam Karpilove's *Yudis: a geshikhte fun liebe un leyden* (1911), translated here as *Judith: a tale of love and woe.* When we meet her, she is a small-town teenager infatuated with the city boy, Joseph, who came to her town for his cousin's wedding. Joseph, a child of wealthy parents who look down their noses on Judith's family, is a political organizer and revolutionary engaged in illegal activity, in and out of jail for his agitation. An initial romantic encounter culminates in kisses that "sealed the bond between our two hearts." (p.14) Where Joseph is seemingly passionate about radical politics because it is trendy among his social set, Judith feels the consequences of such politics on a much more visceral level after she witnesses a pogrom that destroys her family's livelihood and takes her father's life.

The letters that form the basis of the novel are all in Judith's voice, and we are told in the introduction that they were found in Jacob's possession after his suicide. The letters chronicle a relationship over many years as Judith and Joseph carry on a secret long-distance romance and plan to smuggle themselves over the border together and make their way to America. Joseph makes a cowardly last-minute decision to remain behind, Judith doubts Joseph's

---

2 See Faith Hillis, *Utopia's Discontents.*

loyalty, and their pledges of friendship and promises of eternal love go unfulfilled. Ultimately, Judith succumbs to tuberculosis before the lovers are able to reconcile. The letters betray the frustrations of Judith's limited knowledge of Joseph's activities and whereabouts, as well as the stress to their youthful romance caused by anti-Jewish violence, Joseph's political activities, and Judith's emigration.

Because of the personal nature of the letters, the focus of the narration is often not directly on these larger political upheavals. They serve as context for Karpilove's primary concern as a writer of romance: the dramas of the heart. Theirs is a tragic love story, filled with affection, doubt, longing, desire, anger and betrayal. Judith's letters are often assertively non-political, even opposed to the ways that political commitments wreak havoc on the redemptive possibilities of love. Although Judith voices the necessity for radical politics in the form of self-defense against antisemitic violence, she is skeptical about the influence Joseph's revolutionary friends have on him, pulling him toward fighting for universal good and away from the promises he has made to her. She is wary of Russian revolutionaries as potentially antisemitic and calls Joseph to bear witness to the destructiveness of a pogrom in a passage reminiscent of Chaim Nachman Bialik's famed pogrom poem, "In the City of Slaughter" (1903) [p. 46]. Moreover, she feels expendable in the face of the larger world of radical youth activism from which she is emotionally, culturally, and intellectually distant as well as—crucially—physically distant. Joseph's revolutionary involvement ruins Judith's chances of a satisfying and joyful love story.

This approach, pitting revolutionary politics against romantic love, may feel counterintuitive. After all, it is often the case in modern Jewish literature that romantic love and Jewish modernity are intertwined ideals. As modern Jewish literature scholar Naomi Seidman notes, modern romance and marriage choice were radical concepts within traditional Jewish society, opposed to the embeddedness of the institution of marriage within a framework that saw it as the unification of families of a similar class in order to consolidate material and social resources and advantages. A romantic plot pairs romantic desire with the teleology of progress and modernity, moving away from traditionalism toward something more radical.[3] But in the case of Miriam Karpilove's *Judith*, the "blocking figures" who seek to prevent the love between the protagonist are not only Joseph's parents, conservative holdouts who don't want Joseph to marry into a lower class, but also Joseph's revolutionary friends who look down on small-town Judith as not intellectual or radical enough for their political circles. In aligning radical youth

---

3   Naomi Seidman, *The Marriage Plot, Or, How Jews Fell in Love with Love, and with Literature.* (Stanford University Press, 2016).

culture with traditional class interests, Karpilove asserts that a woman in love is the most tragic figure, disempowered and disregarded by the left and the right.

Miriam Karpilove (1888–1956) would later sharpen this message about women's precarity in the face of love, especially in radical Jewish youth culture, and this would become a signature feature of her prolific writing career—especially her most well-known work, *Diary of a Lonely Girl, or the Battle against Free Love* (1918). Karpilove's pioneering writing about women and love offers a window into the lived experiences of women in Yiddish-speaking radical circles, for whom a feeling of possibility and social transformation was curtailed by the ever-present limitations placed on them by the misogyny of self-proclaimed revolutionaries.

Born in a town outside of Minsk, Karpilove immigrated to the United States in 1905, where she settled in New York and also spent significant time in Bridgeport, Connecticut, where several of her brothers lived. Her work was popular and oriented toward the concerns and perspectives of women. *Yudis* (1911) was one of Karpilove's first published works, following on the heels of her play *In di shturem teg* (1909), and it represents one of her earliest attempts to express through her preferred genre of romance fiction her disillusionment with the gender dynamics of radical Jewish youth culture.

*
* *

On September 6, 1955, a year before her death, Miriam Karpilove reflected on her writing career in a letter written in English to her lifelong friend Rose Shomer Bachelis. Reflecting on Shomer Bachelis's recent publication of her memoirs, Karpilove expresses her desire to record her own life story. But she reminds herself, "I gave so many parts of *me* in a number of novels. Now, if I should want to unite the parts, I have to go thru [sic] all of them to put it together."

Of all the things she published throughout her prolific writing career, the piece that Karpilove identified most strongly with was *Yudis: a geshikhte fun liebe un leyden*, translated here as *Judith: a tale of love and woe.* Writing to Shomer Bachelis, Karpilove recalls "that your mother . . . used to call me *Yudis*, instead of Miriam. I liked it." [4] Karpilove appreciated that Shomer Bachelis's mother remembered her novel and routinely associated the author with its title character.

It's no wonder that *Judith* was close to Karpilove's heart and that she recalled it affectionately even at the end of her life. The protagonist of *Judith* immigrates to America at about the same age, and in the same historical moment, that Karpilove herself left her parents and home in

---

4 Miriam Karpilove, letter to Rose Shomer Bachelis, September 6, 1955. Rose Shomer Bachelis papers, YIVO.

search of safety and opportunity. The events of the novel are drawn from Karpilove's own experiences coming of age amidst political upheaval.[5] Karpilove emigrated from Minsk to the United States in 1905, and her fierce lifelong commitment to Labor Zionism emerged from the heady and desperate atmosphere of Jewish self-defense organizing during a time of rising anti-Jewish violence, the same kind of organizing that Judith participates in following a pogrom in her town. Like Judith, Karpilove continued to correspond with and send money home to her family upon arrival in America, and, also like Judith, Karpilove was a prolific and impassioned writer of letters.

Karpilove's debut as a writer is intertwined with her early political involvement. Upon settling in Bridgeport, Connecticut alongside several of her brothers in 1905, Karpilove became secretary for the Bridgeport branch of the Poale Tsiyen Labor Zionist movement, for which her close friend and correspondent A. Halpern served as president. The relationship between Halpern and Karpilove is unclear from the archival record, but Halpern worked in a photography studio and it seems likely Karpilove worked with him for a time, as she was trained as a photographic

---

5 Karpilove's novel can be read as one of the many works of fiction written under the powerful and immediate experience of the 1905 insurrection, in what Jonathan Frankel has referred to as the "instant fictionalization of politics." See Jonathan Frankel, "An-sky's *In Shtrom* and the Instant Fictionalization of 1905" in *Crisis, Revolution, and Russian Jews.* (Cambridge University Press, 2009), 72-97, 72.

retoucher. [6] It appears that Karpilove was recruited and encouraged in her writing by Kalmen Marmur, a fellow Poale Tziyen activist, writer, and editor who was aiming to develop women writers for *der Idisher kemfer,* an organ of Poale Tziyen. [7] It is likely that Halpern had originally connected Karpilove to Marmur, as Halpern and Marmur had long been friends. [8] In his memoirs, Marmur recalls Karpilove as "the tall Bridgeport [photographic] retoucher" who "sent in excellent reports on [political] meetings]," and on the strength of this journalism Marmur encouraged her to write journalistic personal essays and descriptive pieces, eventually leading to her career largely as a writer of serialized newspaper novels and short stories. [9]

Karpilove's family and friends enthusiastically encouraged her burgeoning writing career. In an undated postcard addressed to Karpilove, Halpern praised her as a "clever, clever, clever" woman on account of her writing. [10] In a postcard sent to his sister just hours after she has left Bridgeport and returned to New York, Karpilove's brother Jacob writes, "we'll be waiting in Bridgeport for your first

6 See Harry J. Kahn, *Fuftsik yor Poyle Tsienizm in Amerike* [New York: Farlag Biderman, 1953], 24.

7 See Marmur, Kalman, *Mayn lebns-geshikhte*. Ikuf, 1959, p. 754.

8 Postcard from A. Galperin to Miriam Karpilove, undated. Miriam Karpilow papers, YIVO, Box 3 [those searching MK's archive for this postcard should look for an image on the front of the postcard of an angel playing a viola]

9 Marmur, *Mayn lebns-geshikhte*, 754.

10 Miriam Karpilow papers, YIVO, Folder 7 box 4.

'installment,'" slyly comparing her personal letters to her professional writing while sharing his excitement about her writing talents.[11]

Although the process that led to the publication of *Judith* is not entirely discernable, certain events become clear from Karpilove's correspondence. Karpilove submitted her epistolary novel—which she refers to as "the letters"—with some trepidation and doubt about its possible acceptance. Writing to her sister-in-law Rebecca about the manuscript when it is still under editorial consideration, she complains, "it could take him [Marmur] up to a year to read it. He is terribly slow."[12] At every turn, Halpern offered warm encouragement, asking if her submission had met with success.[13] Likewise, Miriam's sister Dina anxiously wrote to ask, "Has Marmur been to see you yet? . . . you must know by now."[14] Presumably, after a significant wait, Karpilove received a visitor to the boarding room where she was living in Manhattan: Marmur delivered the news in person that her manuscript had been accepted for publication by a small press, Maisel and Co., located on Grand Street. Hers would be the first

11 Postcard from Jacob Karpilow to Miriam Karpilove, dated Friday, March 4, 1938. Miriam Karpilow papers, YIVO, box 3.

12 Miriam Karpilove postcard to Rebecca Karpilow, April 5, 1910. Miriam Karpilow papers, YIVO, box 3.

13 Postcard from Galperin to Miriam Karpilove, January 17, 1911. Miriam Karpilow papers, YIVO, box 3.

14 Dina Karpilow to Miriam Karpilove, undated. Miriam Karpilow papers, YIVO, box 3.

book by a woman to be published by the press, whose catalogue included Yiddish translations of Chekhov, Andreev, Strindberg, Psibishevsky, Maeterlinck and Ibsen and the poetry of Morris Winchevsky. After the book was published, Halpern wrote to Karpilove, describing seeing the physical volume at her brother Jacob's house: "It was very good. The book is much bigger than I would have thought. I wish you much success!"[15] This celebratory tone suggests what a novelty it was for Karpilove's name to appear in print, and the extent to which she already knew that she hoped it would be the first of many.

This early success did indeed lead to many others, as the rate of Karpilove's shorter publications in newspapers steadily increased after the publication of *Judith*. Indeed, *Judith* itself was well circulated. It was, for instance, listed among the books that could be purchased through the book catalogue of the anarchist newspaper *Fraye arbeter shtime*, to which Karpilove herself had begun contributing in a piecemeal fashion by 1913.[16] It likely is not an exaggeration to say that the publication of *Judith* was the turning point in Karpilove's becoming a professional writer. Karpilove went on to become a pioneering woman writer of Yiddish fiction, known for her snide and sharp critique of gender roles and expectations in Yiddish immigrant culture. A prolific author of

---

15 Postcard from Galperin to Miriam Karpolove. Miriam Karpilow papers, YIVO, box 3.
16 See advertisements column, p. 7, *Fraye arbeter shtime*, November 20, 1915.

serialized novels, short stories, sketches, and feuilletons, her work appeared in a variety of Yiddish periodicals over the course of her fifty-year literary career.

I began translating *Judith* a few summers ago, coming off the enormous emotional high of having submitted the manuscript for my own first book-length work, a translation of Karpilove's 1918 novel *Diary of a Lonely Girl, or the Battle against Free Love* (Syracuse University Press, 2020). Having let go of that project so it could make its way in the world, I was already missing the company of Miriam Karpilove's wry sense of humor and her sometimes raw, introspective honesty. I was curious to spend time with her earlier work and get a sense for how her writing developed from her debut endeavors, which tend toward melancholy, to her later writing, which often relies more on her ironic sense of humor.

There's something intimate about reading and translating epistolary work because of the illusion of immediacy and authenticity that novels written as letters give. Each letter could have been written to me, or I could imagine each as something I had discovered in my own attic, and I had the delightful task of playing detective and imagining Judith for myself, bending over a sheet of paper, her tears blurring the ink of her heartfelt words.

I translated rapidly and with intense enjoyment, initially worrying less about accuracy than about replicating this feeling of suspense and discovery.

As it turns out, there were more discoveries awaiting me. A few months later, I made my way to Miriam Karpilove's papers at the YIVO archive, and as I was sifting through postcards and newspaper clippings, I found myself gazing down at a handwritten manuscript of Miriam Karpilove's own English translation of *Judith*, as well as a typewritten copy of that manuscript. Her translation was undated, but her correspondence suggests that later in life, in the mid-1950s, she had begun a project of organizing, compiling, and sometimes translating her writing in the hopes of republishing it and circulating it for new audiences.

It was then that this project became one quite different from my previous experience of translating Miriam Karpilove's work. After rereading and editing my own translation to my satisfaction, I sat down with Karpilove's version and compared hers and mine side-by-side. Here is one example of the differences between her version and mine:

> **Karpilove's version:** Again I see Aaron's delight as he announces that his favorite cousin is coming to his sister's wedding. All are impatient to see you, for much have they heard of you! The evening of

the wedding is here! You have not come! There is a telegram! You are delayed but will come. Sit still my heart! How you beat for a stranger!

My version: It seems just a moment ago when Aaron first came to tell us that his cousin was coming to our town for his sister's wedding. Everyone was anxious to see you as we'd already heard so much about you. When the evening of the wedding arrived you weren't here. Then we received a telegram saying that you were delayed, but on your way! My heart was pounding and I asked myself: What does this guest have to do with *my* heart? (p.12)

A discerning reader will note that these two translations are not enormously divergent in meaning, but vary in tone. Karpilove's use of present tense verbs feels to me like a choice that adheres too closely to conventions of Yiddish writing and makes for uncomfortable reading in English, though perhaps it also adds to the immediacy of the text and makes it more credible as an informal letter. I made a choice to elongate the short sentences for a more even flow that felt somewhat more explanatory than Karpilove's version—my version is about "you" rather than addressed to "you." I felt this made for more comfortable reading, though surely a less dramatic one. Similarly, I have Judith describing her heart rather than addressing it, as I wasn't sure contemporary readers would tolerate the heightened melodrama of Judith asking her own heart to be still.

Occasionally, as I read through Karpilove's translation I found outright mistakes or misinterpretations on my part and allowed Karpilove's version to override mine. But more often than not I had to evaluate her choices alongside my own and decide which was the better fit for my version. Karpilove's English is often beautiful and melodious, but at times it felt overwritten and old fashioned to me, and I was happy to adhere to my own somewhat clippier prose. I was confident, for instance, that I wanted to retain my own restraint with regard to punctuation— Karpilove relied heavily on exclamation points! At other times, her choices felt more idiomatic than mine and I edited accordingly, crossing out, for instance, my "fantastical image" that "disappears" to make way for Karpilove's "vision" that "flies away." [p26] Perhaps most satisfying for me were those heady moments when Karpilove's translation and mine converged almost exactly, word for word, such as when we both translated the same sentence as "in your love for me you overlook my love for you" [p19]. These rare instances when we overlapped precisely felt to me like her manuscript was embracing mine—this is, after all, a romance novel, so my readers will forgive this emotionally laden metaphor—and gave me confidence to follow my instincts with the rest of the translation, feeling that I had understood Karpilove so fully.

There were many cases in which I left Karpilove's version in the margins to be evaluated and considered later, in the same way that I might engage with comments from an editor or friend reading over the manuscript. For my perfectly good "trying to cover up some weakness" I reminded myself in the margins that "Karpilove has: 'merely a cloak for weakness'" to allow myself a wider range of options and to remind myself that I was not alone in the translation, but part of a conversation, even a negotiation, with Miriam Karpilove herself. In this particular instance, after some consideration, Karpilove's version won out. [p. 33] Ultimately, though, this is my own translation. It is informed by Karpilove, but it is also informed by my understanding of contemporary readers and how English language use has changed since Karpilove's translation in the mid-1950s. In making choices, my loyalty had to lie with the reader and their enjoyment and understanding of the text, and not solely with Karpilove's manuscript. These decisions were also informed by the discerning advice of this volume's exemplary editor, Daniel Kennedy, without whose diligence and encouragement this project would not have been possible.

Judith is, in a sense, a novel about translation itself. Not in the sense of translating between languages—as I have done in this English iteration of the Yiddish original—but in that it illustrates the struggles of an individual trying to express herself, make herself understood, and interpret the thoughts and feelings of someone who is both physically and emotionally distant and inscrutable. There are many barriers between the lovers—their divergent expectations about what their relationship should be, their differing valuation of Joseph's revolutionary activity and its social dimensions, Judith's immigration to America—and the letters reach across them. The letters attempt to "span the bridge to our happiness," [p. 61] much like a translation bridging the gap between an audience and a text written in another language. If an idealized form of love is one in which two hearts beat together effortlessly and two minds are in perfect harmony, then this epistolary form of love is a more labored version, in which the writer gropes in the dark towards her lover, trying to make herself known. Like the relationship between an original text and its readers in another language, mediated by a translation, this is a relationship imbued with the knowledge of a distance that cannot entirely be closed.

One of the challenges of translating Karpilove is her subtle shifts in tone, from hopeful to melancholic, sometimes tinged with irony, which can at times feel like two separate Karpiloves that need to be accounted for and translated differently. Karpilove explains these mood shifts in her earliest writing for *der Idisher kemfer* in a piece titled "*Fraynd mayner—ikh*"(1907) or, as an unpublished, undated handwritten translation of the piece in her archive styles it, "A letter to oneself."[17] Here, Karpilove describes her melancholy self-reflectiveness: "Horrible oppressiveness, heavy darkness drive me into myself . . . Life becomes a burden." She describes her internal experience as one of self-alienation, observing the world from an emotional remove and then throwing herself into it with a strong desire to accomplish great things and fulfill fantastic desires, which are then only dashed by reality. In the piece, she confesses to bewildering, sometimes contradictory shifts in self-perception: "It seems to me that I *am* strong. Often so strong that I begin to feel weak . . . I feel the strength reasserts itself and having no means of escape, threatens to burst, destroy, annihilate." Readers who have already discovered Miriam Karpilove through my translation of *Diary of a Lonely Girl* may be surprised by this melancholy, as that book contains much more ironic eyerolling and even physical comedy at the expense of buffoon-like lovers. But even in that more upbeat novel the narrator has depressive episodes in which she visualizes her own death.[18] Giving voice to these mood shifts and honoring the rich psychological portrait they convey

17 Miriam Karpilove, "Fraynd mayner—ikh." *Der Idisher Kemfer*, No. 11. June 14, 1907, pp. 10-12; undated translation in Miriam Karpilow papers, YIVO, box 1. Thank you to Amanda Miriam-Khaye Segal for her assistance in procuring the Yiddish original.

18 For one example of suicidal thoughts in *Diary of a Lonely Girl*, see Miriam Karpilove, Diary

of a woman experiencing both highs and lows has been a distinct challenge.

In *Judith*, the protagonist likewise describes a bifurcated personality herself when she writes, "I feel like I am two different people: the person I show the outside world, and the person I am inside . . . The inner one is jealous of the outer one." [p. 22] Sometimes Judith tries to put on a brave face for Joseph, while other times she reveals the barest truth about her loneliness: "I avoided others and locked myself in my longing for you . . . The laughter and songs that surrounded me only made me feel more lonely and desolate." [p. 63] It has been my challenge to discern which of these moods Judith is expressing as she writes. Is she the ardent, animated user of exclamation points who declares "I love you, do you understand? You and you alone!" [p. 19] or the cold, jaded correspondent who writes that it is very "practical" of her lover to give over so little room to his feelings for her, instead inquiring about intellectual life among immigrants in America? [p. 71] Often these moods compete with one another in the same letter, dejectedness hiding just underneath fierce declarations of love and hope. Judith expresses her despair at having been caught up in a love that drains her emotional resources, but she also fights back with barbed comments that suggest she is very much aware of

of a Lonely Girl, or the Battle against Free Love, trans. Jessica Kirzane. [Syracuse University Press, 2020], 166.

her position as a victim not only of political turmoil and antisemitism, but also of love.

Judith's shifts in mood are owing not only to the personalities of the writer and her subject but also the nature of the relationship she pursues. *Judith* is a tragedy of communication, in which "each letter was a new disappointment." Judith does not know whether or how to communicate her love, the most intimate facet of herself. How can Judith be expected to know for certain how she feels about Joseph when she does not know his behavior and does not trust that he is faithful to her? The letters, published without their answers, present Joseph as unreliable and suspect. Judith's circumstances are precarious as she gives up her prospects of marriageability while waiting for Joseph to make good on his promises, tragically wasting her life away, even as her letters to Joseph become colder as she tries to hide the severity of her illness from him. In doubting and becoming estranged from her lover, she becomes estranged from her own self, the inner self who "wanted to cry out, but I couldn't" (p.109). She cannot translate her feelings to the page, and she believes that even if they were read, the transmission from the page to their reader's heart would fail to be an accurate and full translation that would unite the lovers' souls.

Despite this impossibility of fully communicating herself, Judith—and Karpilove through her—profoundly tries to reach through her melancholy and touch her readers. She successfully conveys the personal and political dimensions of her experience: her lovelorn, emotional highs and lows as well as her disappointments that revolutionary politics are not directed to free her, even though she never seems certain these messages will fully reach her audience. It has been my great fortune to have the opportunity to carry their efforts, however imperfectly and impossibly, to a new English language readership.

Acknowledgements

I am grateful to several people who encouraged me to pursue this project. Firstly, I cannot imagine being inspired to take on any of this work if I were not part of the *In geveb* team, who I value deeply as co-workers and friends. My students in two "Women Who Wrote in Yiddish" courses helped me understand the importance of this work, and fellow feminist scholar translators, among them Faith Jones, Hinde Burstin, Anita Norich and Irena Klepfisz paved the way with their mentorship and by their example. Thank you also to Miriam Karpilow, David Karpilow, and other members of the extended Karpilow family who have so warmly encouraged and supported this work.

Mindl Cohen read and commented on an early draft and encouraged me to keep going with it. Rachel Beth Gross read and commented on several versions of the introduction and is a precious *khevruse* whose advice I depend upon. Daniel Kennedy offered to publish the translation before I even had a chance to ask and I could not imagine a happier home for it. Thank you to Daniel for your editorial work on this piece, as well as on so many other projects we've shared—it is a joy to learn from you and work with you.

Sam and Debbie Kirzner are endlessly encouraging. Rebecca Kirzner cross stitched a portrait of Miriam Karpilove, feeding my obsession with this author, who I am increasingly certain would have adored being memorialized in stitchwork.

Daniel Kirzane read every word of this book and is always supportive in every way: our two hearts beat together effortlessly and our minds are in perfect harmony, almost all of the time. Jeremiah and Esther give me reasons to write, and reasons to look up from my writing to enjoy a world where everything, even ice cream, is possible.

An excerpt from this translation appeared in the 2020 *Pakn Treger* Digital Translation Issue under the title "You Should Have Been There." I am grateful to Mindl Cohen and Abigail Weaver for their work in editing that excerpt.

Miriam Karpilove

Miriam Karpilove (1888-1956) was a Yiddish novelist and short story author. Her parodies, dramas, poetry, stories and novels appeared in a wide variety of newspapers including *Idisher kempfer*, *Der groyser kibitser*, *Kundes*, *Varhayt*, *Tsukunft*, *Fraye arbeter shtime*, *Tog*, and *Forverts*. Her book-length works include *In di shturem teg* [In the tumultuous days] (1909), *Yudis* [Judith], (1911), *Tage-bukh fun a elende meydl* [Diary of a Lonely Girl] (1918); *Brokhe, a kleyn shtedteldige* [Brokhe, a small-town girl] (1923), and *A provints-tsaytung* [A Provincial Newspaper] (1926), as well as numerous novels that appeared in the daily New York press. Born in Minsk, Karpilove emigrated to the United States in 1905 and was based in New York and Bridgeport, CT for the majority of her career.

Karpilove in English Translation

Diary of a Lonely Girl, or the Battle against Free Love, Syracuse University Press, 2020.

Jessica Kirzane is the assistant instructional professor of Yiddish at the University of Chicago and the editor-in-chief of *In geveb: A Journal of Yiddish Studies.* She is the translator of Miriam Karpilove's *Diary of a Lonely Girl, or the Battle against Free Love* (Syracuse University Press, 2020).

FARLAG

Farlag Press is an independent publisher run by a collective of translators and literature-lovers. We prioritise translations from stateless and minority languages, as well as the writings of exiles, immigrants and other outsiders.

We are a strictly for-loss company, though we are registered as a non-profit association in France.

www.farlag.com

Also Available
1. Moyshe Nadir *Messiah in America (A Drama in Five Acts)*
Translated by Michael Shapiro
144pp ISBN: 9791096677047

Forthcoming titles:

Zusman Segalovitsh *Tsilke the Wild*
Translated by Daniel Kennedy

Farlag Bilingual Series:

1. Hersh Dovid Nomberg *À qui la faute ?* װער איז שולדיק
(Édition bilingue: yiddish/français)
Traduit par Fleur Kuhn-Kennedy
66pp ISBN: 9791096677085

2. Hersh Dovid Nomberg *Between Parents* צווישן טאטע־מאמע
(Bilingual edition: Yiddish/English)
Translated by Ollie Elkus and Daniel Kennedy
74pp ISBN: 9791096677092